An English Christmas

Also by John Julius Norwich

Mount Athos (with Reresby Sitwell, 1966)
The Normans in the South (1967)
Sahara (1968)
The Kingdom in the Sun (1970)
A History of Venice: The Rise to Empire (1977)
A History of Venice: The Greatness and the Fall (1981)
Fifty Years of Glyndebourne (1985)
A Taste for Travel (1985)
The Architecture of Southern England (1985)
A History of Byzantium: The Early Centuries (1988)
Venice: A Traveller's Companion (1990)
A History of Byzantium: The Apogee (1991)
A History of Byzantium: The Decline and Fall (1995)
A Short History of Byzantium (1997)
The Twelve Days of Christmas (1998)
Shakespeare's Kings (1999)
Paradise of Cities: Venice in the Nineteenth Century (2003)
The Middle Sea: A History of the Mediterranean (2006)
Trying to Please (2008)
The Popes: A History (2011)
A History of England in 100 Places (2011)
Sicily: A Short History (2015)
Four Princes: Henry VIII, Francis I, Charles V, Suleiman the Magnificent

Edited by John Julius Norwich

Great Architecture of the World (1975)
The Italian World (1983)
Britain's Heritage (1983)
The New Shell Guides to Great Britain (1987–90)
The Oxford Illustrated Encyclopaedia of Art (1990)
The Treasures of Britain (2002)
The Duff Cooper Diaries (2005)
The Great Cities in History (2009)
Darling Monster (2013)
Cities that Shaped the Ancient World (2014)

An English Christmas

JOHN JULIUS NORWICH

JOHN MURRAY

First published in Great Britain in 2017 by John Murray (Publishers)
An Hachette UK company

1

Copyright © John Julius Norwich 2017
Robin illustrations © Christopher Brown

A CIP catalogue record for this title is available from the British Library

ISBN 978-1-473-66592-7
eBook ISBN 978-1-473-66594-1

Typeset in Bembo MT by Hewer Text UK Ltd, Edinburgh
Printed and bound by Clays Ltd, St Ives plc

John Murray policy is to use papers that are natural, renewable and
recyclable products and made from wood grown in sustainable forests.
The logging and manufacturing processes are expected to conform
to the environmental regulations of the country of origin.

John Murray (Publishers)
Carmelite House
50 Victoria Embankment
London EC4Y 0DZ

www.johnmurray.co.uk

To my dear agent Felicity Bryan who got me off the ground

Contents

CONTENTS

CONTENTS

Introduction

Christmas – or something very like it – was thousands of years old by the time Jesus Christ was born, and no wonder: humanity has always celebrated a midwinter festival. On or around the shortest day of the year we all need cheering up; and fortunately, in earliest times, this was about the only time of year that we might expect a fairly plentiful supply of fresh meat, as the farmers slaughtered the livestock that they would be unable to feed in the hungry months to come. And there was another reason too, in which many found consolation: that most of the wine and beer made during the year would now be nicely fermented and ready for drinking, so that we could make a really good feast of it.

Yuletide, Saturnalia, Hogmanay – almost every religion, every civilisation of the cold North has taken the idea to their hearts; but the Christians have made a far better job of it than anyone else. They were not content with settling for Christmas as just a winter tradition; instead, they welded it into the very fabric of their religion, making it Christ's birthday. No one of course has the foggiest idea when he was actually born; but who cares? Like the Queen, he has an official birthday which suits us, and that's what counts.

I have celebrated a good many Christmasses of my own – that of 2017 will be my eighty-eighth – and I have always been fascinated, occasionally enchanted and sometimes faintly appalled by the wildly extravagant trappings that have grown up around this former pagan barbecue. Already in 1377, guests at the first Christmas feast given by King Richard II were consuming a total of twenty-eight oxen and three hundred sheep; it must have been quite a party. But, inevitably, there have been other rulers who preferred something simpler; Oliver Cromwell, indeed, went rather too far in his Puritan way and banned Christmas altogether; but this was not a success, and there were protests all over the country. In some towns, it was said, there was more holly and mistletoe to be seen than before the Commonwealth began, and the formerly innocent carols – now transformed into songs of protest – were bellowed out with such raucous enthusiasm that on Christmas Day 1656 members of parliament complained that they had been kept awake all night by the noise. One suspects, even then, that the celebrations four years later, after the return of Charles II, may have been noisier still.

The festival that they knew, however, would have been very different from what it is today, for Christmas as we know it is a largely nineteenth-century phenomenon, the joint invention of two very different men: Albert, the Prince Consort, and Charles Dickens. It was Albert who popularised the Christmas tree; the tradition of the Yule log, a huge block of wood which was kept burning throughout the twelve days of Christmas, was already known in England and went back, probably, to Anglo-Saxon times; but the idea of bringing a whole tree into the house, not to burn but to decorate and to make the centre for the exchange of presents, was unknown in England until his day. (The Prince is also often wrongly credited with the invention of the Christmas card; but the first bunch of these was despatched in 1843 by Sir Henry Cole – who went on to be responsible, far more than Albert who again took most of the credit, for the Great Exhibition of 1851.) And then there was Dickens. But for him, our traditional Christmas might have remained a royal idiosyncrasy; it is thanks to him, and above all to *A Christmas Carol,* that we know how Christmas *should* be celebrated. It certainly galvanized the Victorians. Upon finishing *A Christmas Carol* reclusive philosopher Thomas Carlyle 'was seized with a perfect convulsion of hospitality, and actually insisted on improvising two dinner parties with only a day between' – cue Jane Carlyle's very amusing letter about her struggles to prepare the turkey. Like the Carlyles we may ourselves fall somewhat short of the ideal. Or, like my Uncle John, we may go well beyond it. Let me explain why.

Everyone has their own idea of Christmas – based, very largely I suspect, on those that they remember from their childhood. With increasing age the annual celebrations become somehow less important, if only because one has gone through so many of them that they seem to have all telescoped together. To a child, on the other hand – and particularly to a child as ridiculously lucky as I was – Christmas was a wonderful thing indeed, looked forward to at least since the previous midsummer. For the first decade of my life, up to the beginning of the Second World War, it was always spent at Belvoir Castle, the home of Uncle John, Duke of Rutland, my mother's older brother. Even now, the scale of his hospitality astonishes me. The entire family would be there, including those of his four siblings, together with several more elderly relations – mostly, as I remember, bachelor uncles and maiden aunts. Nearly all, in those days, would bring their valets and ladies' maids. For lunch and dinner there would thus be twenty or more grown-ups in the dining room, with perhaps a couple of dozen extra in the servants' hall, over and above the countless staff of the Castle itself. Then there were all the children, with their nannies and governesses, divided between the nursery and the schoolroom – perhaps another twenty altogether. All told, there cannot have been fewer than fifty or sixty extra mouths to feed – most of them for more than a week, since we nearly all stayed over the New Year.

The excitement began on around 20 December, with the arrival from the cellar of several enormous cabin trunks to be packed. Looking back on it, I am staggered by the sheer amount of packing that took place, every item meticulously wrapped in tissue paper. By the time it was finished on the 23rd, it took two men to carry the by now unbelievably heavy luggage down to the waiting taxi, in which my parents, my nanny and I took a taxi to King's Cross – in those days still grey, cavernous and caked with grime – and boarded the train to Grantham. It would be pitch dark by the time we arrived at the gas-lit station, where two huge Rolls-Royces lurked ready to receive us. On to these, with the help of a regiment of porters – there was no shortage of them in those days, long before wheel-less suitcases had been invented – the trunks would be slowly and painfully loaded, and off we went. To a five- or six-year-old, still unused to being out at night, the twenty-minute journey was wildly exciting, watching the rabbits scuttling away from the headlights and then suddenly catching one's first sight of that tremendous floodlit castle, standing high and immensely impressive on its hill, visible for miles from any direction. Ten more minutes would bring us to the immense door, from which a short passage led to the entrance hall, known as the Gun Room, its walls bristling with swords, spears and blunderbusses, with, in its centre, the Tree. And what a tree it was – in my memory a good twenty feet high, gloriously decorated, piled with presents and lit with real candles, a hundred or more of them. Liveried footmen, in dark blue tail coats with brass buttons gleaming, stood around holding long poles with wet sponges on the ends, ready to act in an emergency. Then at last to the bedroom that I always shared with Nanny, warmed by a roaring coal fire (no central heating, in that wing at any rate) and on to a quick supper and bed.

The following days were completely traditional: carol singers, Christmas stockings at the foot of the bed, *While Shepherds Watched* and *O Come All Ye Faithful* in the Chapel, opening of presents around the tree, Christmas pudding (how many of them must have been consumed?) and mince pies galore. The rest of our days were taken up with visits to the stables, with apples and lumps of sugar to hold out flat-handed to the horses; to the kennels, slightly less popular merely because the hounds couldn't be fed; to the dairy, with its wonderful milky smell, its butter churns and its huge dishes of cream, where one was given glasses of warm, foaming milk straight from the cow; to the sawmill, where for the first – and very nearly the last – time in my life I planed a piece of wood; and to the forge, where I was allowed to work the bellows. Best of all was the Boxing Day meet of the Belvoir Hunt – all pink coats and excited, yelping dogs and stirrup-cups and ladies sitting bolt upright on side-saddles, with top hats and veils and flowing black skirts descending to the heels of their riding-boots.

Then came New Year's Eve – still very much a part of the Belvoir Christmas – and the huge treat, from the age of about seven or eight, of being allowed to stay up till midnight to sing *Auld Lang Syne* and to see the New Year in. The children didn't actually have dinner with the grown-ups – that would have been purgatory for all involved – but went into the dining room when they had finished but while they were still sipping their port. There would still be an hour and a half or so before midnight, the space being filled by party games. Charades was the favourite, though I personally preferred The Game, which involved trying to express a well-known book title or proverb in dumb show. There was another too, in which two people assumed historical roles and had a short conversation, during which each had to guess the identity of the other. I still remember one session, which lasted only a few seconds. It began with one lady saying 'I think the smell was the worst thing of all.' 'Mrs Noah,' said the other lady, and she was right.

It suddenly dawns on me that as yet I have said not a single word about Father Christmas. Who, I wonder, invented him? He's originally St Nicholas, we all know that. We also know that his body was removed from the church of Myra (now Demre in Turkey, where I have seen his empty grave) but by whom? According to one account, the body-snatchers were sailors from Bari, where a large and most magnificent church – even better than the Cathedral – was erected in his honour; but the Venetians also claim responsibility, firmly maintaining that he is buried in the rather more modest church on the Lido that bears his name, to which the Doge and his *Signoria* took part in a solemn procession every year on his feast day. Oddly enough, both versions may be right: recent scientific investigations suggest that the relics in the two cities may belong to the same body.

But when did St Nicholas become Father Christmas? Probably in the reign of Henry VIII, when he was represented as a fat, jolly, bearded gentleman in scarlet (or sometimes green) robes, trimmed with white fur. As now, he typified the spirit of Christmas good cheer, but there was a lot of work to be done before he assumed the ho-ho-ho shape and figure we know today. All the later accoutrements, the reindeer and the sleigh, the descent down the chimney, the filling of the stockings, all this is nineteenth-century and even early twentieth, with, probably, not a little American influence thrown in.

In a long life – containing plenty of parenthood – I have always managed to avoid dressing up as Father Christmas. My word, how I would have hated it. It was bad enough creeping into my children's bedrooms in the dark to hang up their stockings, always terrified that they would wake up to see what an imposter their father really was. As a boy, I think I managed to maintain my own unquestioning belief until I was five or six. (Shirley Temple used to claim that she lost hers at about the same age, when she met Santa Claus in a large department store and he asked her for her autograph.) Few children, I fear, could say the same today; a single glance at one of those photographs of a Father Christmas reunion – a hundred or so of them all milling around together – would disenchant them for ever.

Christmasses like those we had at Belvoir don't come like that any more, and I'm not sure that I could take them if they did. The world has changed – on the whole, I believe, for the better (though I could perhaps suggest one or two minor improvements). Nowadays Christmas is for me a quiet, family affair, staying with my daughter or step-son – not so exciting, perhaps, as in the old days (how could it be? As birthday succeeds birthday one loses, alas, the capacity for excitement) but every bit as enjoyable. There have been the occasional exceptions; some twenty or thirty years ago Mollie and I spent Christmas on the coast of Kenya, sharing our room with a couple of dozen hermit crabs and frequently meeting a herd of baboons when we went down to swim. The heat was intense, the pudding was late arriving, and we had our Christmas Dinner on the 27th. More recently, by way of contrast, I went with my grand-daughter, my son-in-law Antony Beevor and my son Jason to the Antarctic on a Russian ice-breaker. That was unlike any Christmas I have ever known. It was, very largely, a Christmas of silence. In the world in which we normally live, silence simply doesn't exist. Even when we think we have found it we are, as like as not, subconsciously shutting our ears to the ordinary sounds of nature – the rustle of branches, the trickle of water, the song of a bird. In the Antarctic, even these sounds are exceptions: silence stands no longer as a negative concept but as a present, positive thing, wrapping itself round you like a cloak. Occasionally, however, it would be rudely broken by a party of Finns among our fellow passengers, who daily stripped to the buff and splashed about among the icebergs. The evenings, too, tended to get a trifle noisy – particularly after our Christmas dinner, when we were all asked to song a song. I obliged with one about the Titanic – which, I felt, was only fairly well received.

But there: you won't find much about baboons or icebergs in the pages that follow. Some of the pieces we have chosen will probably be familiar; but I like to think that a good many of them at least will be new to you. I have spread the net as widely as I could: fact and fiction, verse and prose, from the middle ages to the present day. Letters and diaries, I find, are a particularly fruitful source of treasure, diaries in particular (Among these, I would particularly like to draw your attention to the entries by that unlikely pair, the Reverend Francis Kilvert and Sir Cecil Beaton. The two have little enough in common apart from their nationality, but that is enough.)

Which reminds me: perhaps I should say a word about the title of this book, *An English Christmas*; admittedly, not every item is set in England; but whether we are reading about Sir Ernest Shackleton trapped in the polar ice or about Elizabeth David struggling with her Christmas pudding for those profoundly ungrateful French villagers, we are I think always conscious of their essential Englishness. Reading their accounts, we instantly recognise them as our compatriots. For the truth is that Christmas as we know it is still an essentially English feast. Even in America it isn't quite the same, while on the continent of Europe it varies almost wherever you go. The French copy us up to a point, largely because their shops do so well; but their celebrations tend to be in a distinctly lower key than ours, and it is at the New Year that they exchange their presents. (Which even have a special name, *étrennes*. For the rest of the year they are simply *cadeaux*.) To compensate, they make a much bigger thing of Epiphany, a date which is in England so much forgotten that relatively few of the younger generation could, I suspect, even tell you what it is or when it falls. We know it, insofar as we know it at all, as Twelfth Night; for the French, however, and for many other European countries it is the *Fête des Rois*, commemorating the arrival at the manger of the Three Kings, and is quite a celebration – featuring a special cake of puff pastry filled with frangipani cream and containing a small charm, the finder of which becomes King of the Feast and is crowned with a gold paper crown. All very well, one feels, but perhaps a little unEnglish?

8

And so, in the pages that follow, we are sticking firmly to English Christmasses. By no means all of them are a paean of praise to the Feast of the Nativity. George Orwell, Evelyn Waugh and Philip Larkin are only three of those who positively hated it. A good many other people do too. I have one friend who annually travels to deepest Asia in order to escape it, and several others who would probably do so if they could. On the whole, however, the verdict is favourable; the general conclusion is that it is here to stay. For my part I love it dearly: I just wish it didn't come round about every three months.

I leave you with a parting thought from a Christmas card, sent me some years ago by some friends in Jerusalem:

> Roses are red
> Violets are blueish;
> If it wasn't for Christmas
> You'd all be Jewish.

Happy Christmas . . .

John Julius Norwich

ADVENT

Christmas

John Betjeman

The bells of waiting Advent ring,
The Tortoise stove is lit again
And lamp-oil light across the night
Has caught the streaks of winter rain
In many a stained-glass window sheen
From Crimson Lake to Hookers Green.

The holly in the windy hedge
And round the Manor House the yew
Will soon be stripped to deck the ledge,
The altar, font and arch and pew,
So that the villagers can say
'The church looks nice' on Christmas Day.

Provincial Public Houses blaze,
Corporation tramcars clang,
On lighted tenements I gaze,
Where paper decorations hang,
And bunting in the red Town Hall
Says 'Merry Christmas to you all'.

And London shops on Christmas Eve
Are strung with silver bells and flowers
As hurrying clerks the City leave
To pigeon-haunted classic towers,

And marbled clouds go scudding by
The many-steepled London sky.

And girls in slacks remember Dad,
And oafish louts remember Mum,
And sleepless children's hearts are glad.
And Christmas-morning bells say 'Come!'
Even to shining ones who dwell
Safe in the Dorchester Hotel.

And is it true,
This most tremendous tale of all,
Seen in a stained-glass window's hue,
A Baby in an ox's stall?
The Maker of the stars and sea
Become a Child on earth for me?

And is it true? For if it is,
No loving fingers tying strings
Around those tissued fripperies,
The sweet and silly Christmas things,
Bath salts and inexpensive scent
And hideous tie so kindly meant,

No love that in a family dwells,
No carolling in frosty air,
Nor all the steeple-shaking bells
Can with this single Truth compare –
That God was man in Palestine
And lives today in Bread and Wine.

Dinner at the Westons'

from *Emma*, Jane Austen

Mr Woodhouse had so completely made up his mind to the visit, that in spite of the increasing coldness, he seemed to have no idea of shrinking from it, and set forward at last most punctually with his eldest daughter in his own carriage, with less apparent consciousness of the weather than either of the others; too full of the wonder of his own going, and the pleasure it was to afford at Randalls to see that it was cold, and too well wrapt up to feel it. The cold, however, was severe; and by the time the second carriage was in motion, a few flakes of snow were finding their way down, and the sky had the appearance of being so overcharged as to want only a milder air to produce a very white world in a very short time.

Emma soon saw that her companion was not in the happiest humour. The preparing and the going abroad in such weather, with the sacrifice of his children after dinner, were evils, were disagreeables at least, which Mr John Knightley did not by any means like; he anticipated nothing in the visit that could be at all worth the purchase; and the whole of their drive to the vicarage was spent by him in expressing his discontent.

'A man,' said he, 'must have a very good opinion of himself when he asks people to leave their own fireside, and encounter such a day as this, for the sake of coming to see him. He must think himself a most agreeable fellow; I could not do such a thing. It is the greatest absurdity – Actually snowing at this moment! – The folly of not allowing people to be comfortable at home – and the folly of people's not staying comfortably at home when they can! If we were obliged to go out such an evening as this, by any call of duty or business, what a hardship we should deem it; – and here are we, probably with rather thinner clothing than usual, setting forward voluntarily, without excuse, in defiance of the voice of nature, which tells man, in every thing given to his view or his feelings, to stay at home himself, and keep all under shelter that he can; – here are we setting forward to spend five dull hours in another man's house, with nothing to say or to hear that was not said and heard yesterday, and may not be said and heard again tomorrow. Going in dismal weather, to return probably in worse; – four horses and four servants taken out for nothing but to convey five idle, shivering creatures into colder rooms and worse company than they might have had at home.'

Emma did not find herself equal to give the pleased assent, which no doubt he was in the habit of receiving, to emulate the Very true, my love, which must have been usually administered by his travelling companion; but she had resolution enough to refrain from making any answer at all. She could not be complying, she dreaded being quarrelsome; her heroism reached only to silence. She allowed him to talk, and arranged the glasses, and wrapped herself up, without opening her lips.

They arrived, the carriage turned, the step was let down, and Mr Elton, spruce, black, and smiling, was with them instantly [. . .]

'What an excellent device,' said he, 'the use of a sheepskin for carriages. How very comfortable they make it; – impossible to feel cold with such precautions. The contrivances of modern days indeed have rendered a gentleman's carriage perfectly complete. One is so fenced and guarded from the weather, that not a breath of air can find its way unpermitted. Weather becomes absolutely of no consequence. It is a very cold afternoon – but in this carriage we know nothing of the matter. – Ha! snows a little I see.'

'Yes,' said John Knightley, 'and I think we shall have a good deal of it.'

'Christmas weather,' observed Mr Elton. 'Quite seasonable; and extremely fortunate we may think ourselves that it did not begin yesterday, and prevent this day's party, which it might very possibly have done, for Mr Woodhouse would hardly have ventured had there been much snow on the ground; but now it is of no consequence. This is quite the season indeed for friendly meetings. At Christmas every body invites their friends about them, and people think little of even the worst weather. I was snowed up at a friend's house once for a week. Nothing could be pleasanter. I went for only one night, and could not get away till that very day sennight.'

Mr John Knightley looked as if he did not comprehend the pleasure, but said only, coolly, 'I cannot wish to be snowed up a week at Randalls.'

At another time Emma might have been amused, but she was too much astonished now at Mr Elton's spirits for other feelings. Harriet seemed quite forgotten in the expectation of a pleasant party.

'We are sure of excellent fires,' continued he, 'and everything in the greatest comfort. Charming people, Mr and Mrs Weston; – Mrs Weston indeed is much beyond praise, and he is exactly what one values, so hospitable, and so fond of society; – it will be a small party, but where small parties are select, they are perhaps the most agreeable of any. Mr Weston's dining room does not accommodate more than ten comfortably; and for my part, I would rather, under such circumstances, fall short by two than exceed by two. I think you will agree with me, (turning with a soft air to Emma,) I think I shall certainly have your approbation, though Mr Knightley perhaps, from being used to the large parties of London, may not quite enter into our feelings.'

'I know nothing of the large parties of London, sir – I never dine with anybody.'

'Indeed! (in a tone of wonder and pity,) I had no idea that the law had been so great a slavery. Well, sir, the time must come when you will be paid for all this, when you will have little labour and great enjoyment.'

'My first enjoyment,' replied John Knightley, as they passed through the sweep-gate, 'will be to find myself safe at Hartfield again.'

On Christmas

John Bamffylde

With footstep slow, in furry pall y-clad,
His brows enwreathed with holly never sere,
Old Christmas comes, to close the waned year,
And aye the shepherd's heart to make right glad;
Who, when his teeming flocks are homeward
    had,
To blazing hearth repairs, and nut-brown beer;
And views, well pleased, the ruddy prattlers dear
Hug the grey mongrel; meanwhile, maid and lad
Squabble for roasted crabs. Thee, sire, we hail,
Whether thine aged limbs thou dost enshroud
In vest of snowy white and hoary veil,
Or wrapp'st thy visage in a sable cloud;
Thee we proclaim with mirth and cheer, nor fail
To greet thee well with many a carol loud.

How to Stuff a Turkey

Letter from Jane Welsh Carlyle

Jane Welsh Carlyle was the wife of essayist Thomas Carlyle. Their marriage was tempestuous and complicated by other relationships on both sides. This letter is to Jeannie Welsh, dated 28 December 1843.

A thousand thanks my darling for your long good Christmas-letter and also for the prospective footstools. Anything like a worthy answer you have small chance of getting from me today or any day this week; I have just had to swallow a bumper of my Uncle's Madeira – (which is capital drink!) to nerve me for writing at all! A huge boxful of dead animals from the Welshman arriving late on Saturday night together with the visions of Scrooge – had so worked on Carlyle's nervous organization that he has been seized with a perfect convulsion of hospitality, and has actually insisted on improvising two dinner parties with only a day between . . . Now the improvi-sation of dinner parties is all very well for the parties who have to eat them, simply, but for those who have to organize them and help to cook them *c'est autre chose ma chere* (that's another thing, my dear)! I do not remember that I have ever sustained a moment of greater embarrassment in life than yesterday when Helen suggested to me that 'I had better stuff the Turkey – as she had forgotten all about it'! I had never known 'about it'! but as I make it a rule never to exhibit ignorance on any subject *'Devant les domestiques* [before the servants]' for fear of losing their respect – I proceeded to stuff the Turkey with the same air of calm self dependance with which I told her some time ago, when she applied to me, the whole history of the Scotch-free-church dissentions – which up to this hour I have never been able to take in! 'Fortune favours the brave'

– the stuffing proved pleasanter to the taste than any stuffing I ever remember to have eaten – perhaps it was made with quite new ingredients! – I do not know! – yesterday I had hare-soup, the Turkey, Stewed mutton, a bread pudding and mince-pies with Mrs Allan Cunningham, Miss Cunningham and Major Burns (son of the Poet) to eat thereof. On Monday hare soup, roasted-welch, mutton stewed beef ditto pudding ditto pies with Robertson, and John Carlyle, and the disappointment of Darwin – and all that day, to add to my difficulties, I had a headache – so bad that I should have been in bed if I had not had to stay up to help Helen – whose faculties get rusted by disuse—

The Merry Christmas Carnival
from *The London Spy*, Ned Ward

Published in 18 monthly instalments starting in November 1698, The London Spy *by Ned Ward, satirical writer and publican, was described as a 'complete survey' of the London scene, full of racy anecdotes and character sketches.*

The merry Christmas Carnival being now come on . . . we wander'd about like a couple of Runaway Prentices, having confin'd ourselves to no particular Port, *Uncertainty* being our *Course*, and meer *Accident our Pilot*. Every Street we pass'd thro' smelling as strong of Roast-Beef and Rosemary, as *Pye*-Corner does of Pig and Pork, in the Wicked Season of St *Bartholomew*. Every Ale-House we came at was *Seranaded* with a Drum to thunder their Rattle-Headed Customers into a good Humour of spending their Pence like *Asses*, which they got like *Horses*.

Every now and then we came to a common *Vaulting-School*, where peeping in we saw drunked *Tarpaulins* and their Taudry Trulls, Dancing to a *Scotch* Bagpiper, or a blind Fidler; and at least seventeen Strumpets to one that had *Modesty* enough in her Looks to be thought otherwise. Sometimes meeting in the Street with a Boats Crew, just come on Shore, in searc of those Land Debaucheries which the Sea denies 'em; looking like such Wild, Staring, Gamesome, Uncouth Animals, that a Litter of Squab *Rhinocerosses*, drest up in Humane Apparel, could not have made to me a more ungainly Appearance . . . I could not forbear Reflecting on the Prudence of those Persons, who send their *Unlucky Children* to *Sea* to *Tame* and *Reform* 'em, which I am well satisfied, is like sending a *Knave* into *Scotland* to learn *Honesty*; a *Fool* into *Ireland* to learn *Wit* or a *Clown* into *Holland* to learn *Breeding*.

By the Time we had made these Observations and Reflections, we were straggl'd into *Wapping*; and being pretty well tired with our Walk, we went into a Publick–House to Refresh our selves with a *Sneaker of Punch*, which most likely to prove the best Liqour that end of the Town cou'd afford us. The first Figure that accosted us at our Entrance, was a Female *Wappineer*, whose Crimson *Countenance* and *Double Chin*, contain'd within the Borders of a *White Callico-Hood*, made her Fiery Face look, in my fancy, like a round *Red-Hot Iron* glowing in a *Silver Chavendish*.

My Friend having a Sword on, I observed to him she was most respectful, asking him in a Voice as hoarse as *Boatswain*, *What will you please to Drink, Noble Captain?* After we had answe'd her Question, she had soon prepar'd us a little Bowl of Spiritual *Diapente*, which, for want of better, we were forc'd to dispence with. Up the Chimney Corner sat a great hulking Fellow smoking a short Pipe of Stinking *Tobacco*, looking as Melancholly upon the Fire as a Female Wretch does upon a *Smith-field* Pile, when she is brought to be burnt for

High-Treason. By and by in comes my Landlady, and like a true Lover of *Industry*, began to Read him a Lecture against *Laziness*, tormenting the Ears of the poor dejected *Water-Rat*, with severe Reprehension, after the following Manner. *Why, how do you think, John, in your Conscience, I am able to maintain you in this Lazy Life you lead? Thou knowest I have no Money, God help me, but what I Work for, as any Woman in the Parish, therefore, John, it behoves thee to consider I am not able to let thee lye in this Condition. Why, what a Rope ails you, Mother* (reply'd the Fellow), *Why, would you have the Conscience to turn me a Drift now I have spent all my Money on Board you, before I have got me another Voyage? You are as hasty with a Body to turn him out, as a Boatswain in a Storm. Why, but* John (reply'd the Landlady) *dost think to get a Voyage by Smoaking in the Chimney Corner? No* (says John) *but how do you think a Man can look out without a Penny in his Breeches? . . .* To which reply'd the old Beldam, *Why, I would not have thee think what I speak is out of any Ill Will to thee; for as far as I am able: here, there is Six-pence for thee, and Prithee, John, Go and look out, and don't fling it away Idely: For consider these hard Times, 'tis a great deal of Money.* He takes the Six-pence, thanks her; and thus she continues, *There were several Ships going out, bound to the* West-Indies, *that want Men and I know though art as able a Seaman as ever walk'd between* Stem *and* Stern *of a Ship, that any Commander will be glad to Enter thee. As to that, Mother,* says he, *I can speak a proud Word for my self; there is ne'er a Part of a Seaman, from the* Splicing *of a* Cable *to the* Cooking *of the* Kettle, *but what I know as well as the* Boatswain. *Well, Mother, wish me good Luck, I'll try what I can do, as the* Gunner *said to the* Cooks Daughter. She wish'd he might Prosper in his Endeavours, and away he went.

I could not but reflect on the unhappy Lives of these *Salt-Water* kind of *Vagabonds,* who are never at Home, but when they're at Sea, and always are Wandering when they're at Home; and never contented but when they're on Shore: they're never at

Ease till they've receiv'd their Pay, and then never satisfied till they have spent it.

Going Carol-Barking

from *Cider with Rosie*, Laurie Lee

The week before Christmas, when the snow seemed to lie thickest, was the moment for carol-singing; and when I think back to those nights it is to the crunch of snow and to the lights of the lanterns on it. Carol-singing in my village was a special tithe for the boys, the girls had little to do with it. Like haymaking, blackberrying, stone-clearing and wishing-people-a-happy-Easter, it was one of our seasonal perks.

By instinct we knew just when to begin it; a day too soon and we should have been unwelcome, a day too late and we should have received lean looks from people whose bounty was already exhausted. When the true moment came, exactly balanced, we recognised it and were ready.

So as soon as the wood had been stacked in the oven to dry for the morning fire, we put on our scarves and went out through the streets calling loudly between our hands, till the various boys who knew the signal ran out from their houses to join us.

One by one they came stumbling over the snow, swinging their lanterns around their heads, shouting and coughing horribly.

'Coming carol-barking then?'

We were the Church Choir, so no answer was necessary. For a year we had praised the Lord, out of key, and as a reward for this service – on top of the Outing – we now had the right to visit all the big houses, to sing our carols and collect our tribute.

Eight of us set out that night. There was Sixpence the Tanner, who had never sung in his life (he just worked his mouth in church); The brothers Horace and Boney, who were always fighting everybody and always getting the worst of it; Clergy Green, the preaching maniac; Walt the bully, and my two brothers. As we went down the lane, other boys, from other villages, were already about the hills, bawling 'Kingwensluch', and shouting through keyholes 'Knock on the knocker! Ring at the Bell! Give us a penny for singing so well!' They weren't an approved charity as we were, the Choir; but competition was in the air.

Our first call as usual was the house of the Squire, and we trooped nervously down his drive. For light we had candles in marmalade jars suspended on loops of string, and they threw pale gleams on the towering snowdrifts that stood on each side of the drive. A blizzard was blowing, but we were well wrapped up, with Army puttees on our legs, woollen hats on our heads, and several scarves around our ears. As we approached the Big House across its white silent lawns, we too grew respectfully silent. The lake nearby was stiff and black, the waterfall frozen and still. We arranged ourselves shuffling around the big front door, then knocked and announced the Choir.

A maid bore the tidings of our arrival away into the echoing distances of the house. The door was left ajar and we were bidden to begin. We brought no music, the carols were in our heads. 'Let's give 'em "Wild Shepherds",' said Jack. We began in confusion, plunging into a wreckage of keys, of different words and tempos; but we gathered our strength; he who sang loudest took the rest of us with him, and the carol took shape if not sweetness.

This huge stone house, with its ivied walls, was always a mystery to us. What were those gables, those rooms and attics, those narrow windows veiled by the cedar trees? As we sang

'Wild Shepherds' we craned our necks aping into that lamplit hall which we had never entered; staring at the muskets and untenanted – until suddenly, on the stairs, we saw the old Squire himself standing and listening with his head on one side. He didn't move until we'd finished; then slowly he tottered towards us, dropped two coins in our box with a trembling hand, scratched his name in the book we carried, give us each a long look with his moist blind eyes, then turned away in silence. As though released from a spell, we took a few sedate steps, then broke into a run for the gate. We didn't stop till we were out of the grounds. Impatient, at least, to discover the extent of his bounty, we squatted by the cowsheds, held our lanterns over the book, and saw that he'd written 'Two Shillings'. This was quite a good start. No one of any worth in the district would dare to give us less than the Squire.

Crossing, at last, the frozen mill-stream – whose wheel in summer still turned a barren mechanism – we climbed up to Joseph's farm. Sheltered by trees, warm on its bed of snow, it seemed always to be like this. As always it was late; as always this was our final call. The snow had a fine crust upon it, and the old trees sparkled like tinsel. We grouped ourselves round the farmhouse porch. The sky cleared, and broad streams of stars ran down over the valley and away to Wales. On Slad's white slopes, seen through the black sticks of its woods, some red lamps still burned in the windows. Everything was quiet; everywhere there was the faint crackling silence of the winter night. We started singing, and we were all moved by the words and the sudden trueness of our voices. Pure, very clear, and breathless we sang:

> As Joseph was a walking
> He heard an angel sing;
> This night shall be the birth-time
> Of Christ the Heavenly King.

He neither shall be bornèd
In Housen nor in hall,
Not in a place of paradise
But in an ox's stall . . .

And two thousand Christmases became real to us then; the houses, the halls, the places of paradise had all been visited; the stars were bright to guide the Kings through the snow; and across the farmyard we could hear the beasts in their stalls. We were given roast apples and hot mince-pies, in our nostrils were spices like myrrh, and in our wooden box, as we headed back for the village, there were golden gifts for all.

Dear Mr Spectator

MR. *SPECTATOR*,

I am a young woman, and have my Fortune to make, for which Reason I come constantly to Church to hear divine Service, and make Conquests; but one great Hindrance in this my Design is, that our Clerk, who was once a Gardener, has this Christmas so over-decked the Church with Greens, that he has quite spoil'd my Prospect, insomuch that I have scarce seen the young Baronet I dress at these three Weeks, though we have both been very Constant at our Devotions, and do not sit above three Pews off. The Church, as it is now equipped, looks more like a Green-house than a Place of Worship; the middle Isle is a very pretty Shady Walk, and the Pews look like so many Arbours on each Side of it. The Pulpit itself has such Clusters of Ivy, Holly, and Rosemary about it, that a light Fellow in our Pew took Occasion to say, that the Congregation heard the Word

out of a Bush, like *Moses*. Sir *Anthony Love's* Pew in particular is so well hedg'd, that all my Batteries have no Effect.
I am obliged to shoot at Random among the Boughs,
without taking any Manner of Aim. Mr. *Spectator*, unless
you will give Orders for removing these Greens, I shall
grow a very aukward Creature at Church, and soon have
little Else to do there but say my Prayers. I am in Haste,

Dear Sir,

Your most obedient Servant,

Jenny Simper.

MR. *SPECTATOR,*

I am Clerk of the Parish from whence Mrs. *Simper* sends
her Complaint, in your yesterday's *Spectator*. I must beg of
you to publish this as a publick Admonition to the aforesaid
Mrs. *Simper*, otherwise all my honest Care in the Disposition
of the Greens in the Church will have no Effect: I shall
therefore with your Leave lay before you the whole Matter.
I was formerly, as she charges me, for several Years a Gardener
in the County of *Kent*; but I must absolutely deny, that it is
out of any Affection I retain for my old Employment that I
have placed my Greens so liberally about the Church, but
out of a Particular Spleen I conceived against Mrs. *Simper*,
and others of the same Sisterhood, some Time ago. As to
herself, I had one Day set the hundredth Psalm, and was
singing the first Line in order to put the Congregation into
the Tune, she was all the While curtsying to Sir *Anthony*, in
so affected and indecent a Manner, that the Indignation I
conceiv'd made me forget myself so far, as from the Tune of
that Psalm to wander into *Southwell*-tune, and from thence
into *Windsor*-tune, still unable to recover myself, until I had
with the utmost Confusion set a new one. Nay, I have often
seen her rise up and smile, and curtsy to one at the Lower
End of the Church, in the midst of a *Gloria-Patri*; and when

I have spoke the Assent to a Prayer with a long *Amen*, uttered with a Decent Gravity, she has been rolling her Eyes about in such a Manner, as plainly shew'd, however she was moved, it was not towards an Heavenly Object. In fine, she extended her Conquests so far over the Males, and rais'd such Envy in the Females, that what between Love of those, and the Jealousy of these, I was almost the only Person that looked in a Prayer-book all Church-time. I had several Projects in my Head to put a Stop to this Growing Mischief; but as I have long lived in *Kent*, and there often heard how the *Kentish* men evaded the Conquerour, by carrying green Boughs over their Heads, it put me in Mind of practising this Device against Mrs. *Simper*. I find I have preserv'd many a Young Man from her Eye-shot by this Means; therefore humbly pray the Boughs may be fix'd, until she shall give Security for her Peaceable Intentions.

Your humble Servant,
Francis Sternhold.

from *South: The Story of Shackleton's Last Expedition,*

Ernest Shackleton

Sir Ernest Shackleton was a polar explorer who led three British expeditions to the Antarctic. The Imperial Trans-Antarctic Expedition (1914–17), was an attempt to make the first land crossing of the Antarctic continent. On 21 November 1915, the ice of the South Ocean finally sank HMS Endurance.

December 15, 1915 – The continuance of southerly winds is exceeding our best hopes, and raising our spirits in proportion.

Prospects could not be brighter than they are just now. The environs of our floe are continually changing. Some days we are almost surrounded by small open leads, preventing us from crossing over to the adjacent floes.

After two more days our fortune changed, and a strong north-easterly wind brought a beastly cold, windy day and drove us back three and a quarter miles. Soon, however, the wind once more veered to the south and south-west. These high temperatures, combined with the strong changeable winds that we had had of late, led me to conclude that the ice all around us was rotting and breaking up and that the moment of our deliverance from the icy maw of the Antarctic was at hand.

On December 20, after discussing the question with Wild, I informed all hands that I intended to try and make a march to the west to reduce the distance between us and Paulet Island. A buzz of pleasurable anticipation went round the camp, and every one was anxious to get on the move. So the next day I set off with Wild, Crean, and Hurley, with dog teams, to the westward to survey the route. After travelling about seven miles we mounted a small berg, and there as far as we could see stretched a series of immense flat floes from half a mile to a mile across, separated from each other by pressure-ridges which seemed easily negotiable with pick and shovel. The only place that appeared likely to be formidable was a very much cracked-up area between the old floe that we were on and the first of the series of young flat floes about half a mile away.

December 22 was therefore kept as Christmas Day, and most of our small remaining stock of luxuries was consumed at the Christmas feast. We could not carry it all with us, so for the last time for eight months we had a really good meal – as much as we could eat. Anchovies in oil, baked beans, and jugged hare made a glorious mixture such as we have not dreamed of since our school-days. Everybody was working at high pressure, packing and repacking sledges and stowing what provisions we were going to take with us in the various sacks and boxes. As I looked round at the eager faces of the men I could not but hope that this time the fates would be kinder to us than in our last attempt to march across the ice to safety.

With the exception of the night-watchman we turned in at 11 p.m., and at 3 a.m. on December 23 all hands were roused for the purpose of sledging the two boats, the James Caird and the Dudley Docker, over the dangerously cracked portion to the first of the young floes, whilst the surface still held its night crust. A thick sea-fog came up from the west, so we started off finally at 4.30 a.m., after a drink of hot coffee.

Practically all hands had to be harnessed to each boat in succession, and by dint of much careful manipulation and tortu-ous courses amongst the broken ice we got both safely over the danger-zone [. . .]

We turned in at 7 p.m. that night, and at 1 a.m. next day, the 25th, and the third day of our march, a breakfast of sledging ration was served. By 2 a.m. we were on the march again. We wished one another a merry Christmas, and our thoughts went back to those at home. We wondered, too, that day, as we sat down to our lunch of stale, thin bannock and a mug of thin cocoa, what they were having . . .

How to Serve Up a Boar's Head
from *The Art of Cookery,*
an Imitation of Horace's Art of Poetry
William King

At Christmas time be careful of your Fame,
See the old Tenant's Table be the same;

Then if you wou'd send up the Brawner's Head,
Sweet Rosemary and Bays around it spread:
His foaming tusks let some large Pippin grace,
Or 'midst these thund'ring Spears an Orange place,
Sauce like himself, offensive to its Foes,
The Roguish Mustard, dang'rous to the Nose.
Sack and the well-spic'd *Hippocras* the Wine,
Wassail the Bowl with antient Ribbands fine,
Porridge with Plumbs, and Turkeys with the Chine . . .

Christmas Shopping on Oxford Street

from *The London Scene*, Virginia Woolf

Down in the docks one sees things in their crudity, their bulk,
their enormity. Here in Oxford Street they have been refined
and transformed. The barrels of damp tobacco have been rolled
into innumerable neat cigarettes laid in silver paper. The corpu-
lent bales of wool have been spun into thin vests and soft stockings. The grease of sheep's thick wool has become scented cream
for delicate skins. And those who buy and those who sell have
suffered the same city change. Tripping, mincing, in black coats,
in satin dresses, the human form has adapted itself no less than
the animal product. Instead of hauling and heaving, it deftly
opens drawers, rolls out silk on counters, measures and snips
with yardsticks and scissors.

Oxford Street, it goes without saying, is not London's most
distinguished thoroughfare. Moralists have been known to point
the finger of scorn at those who buy there, and they have the
support of the dandies. Fashion has secret crannies off Hanover
Square, round about Bond Street, to which it withdraws

discreetly to perform its more sublime rites. In Oxford Street there are too many bargains, too many sales, too many goods marked down to one and eleven three that only last week cost two and six. The buying and selling is too blatant and raucous. But as one saunters towards the sunset – and what with artificial light and mounds of silk and gleaming omnibuses, a perpetual sunset seems to brood over the Marble Arch – the garishness of the great rolling ribbon of Oxford Street has its fascination. It is like the pebbly bed of a river whose stones are for ever washed by a bright stream.

Everything glitters and twinkles. The first spring day brings out barrows frilled with tulips, violets, daffodils in brilliant layers. The frail vessels eddy vaguely across the stream of the traffic. At one corner seedy magicians are making slips of coloured paper expand in magic tumblers into bristling forests of splendidly tinted flora – a subaqueous flower garden. At another, tortoises repose on litters of grass. The slowest and most contemplative of creatures display their mild activities on a foot or two of pavement, jealously guarded from passing feet.

One infers that the desire of man for the tortoise, like the desire of the moth for the star, is a constant element in human nature. Nevertheless, to see a woman stop and add a tortoise to her string of parcels is perhaps the rarest sight that human eyes can look upon.

Taking all this into account – the auctions, the barrows, the cheapness, the glitter – it cannot be said that the character of Oxford Street is refined.

It is a breeding ground, a forcing house of sensation. The pavement seems to sprout horrid tragedies; the divorces of actresses, the suicides of millionaires occur here with a frequency that is unknown in the more austere pavements of the residential districts. News changes quicker than in any other part of London.

The press of people passing seems to lick the ink off the placards and to consume more of them and to demand fresh supplies of later editions faster than elsewhere. The mind becomes a glutinous slab that takes impressions and Oxford Street rolls off upon it a perpetual ribbon of changing sights, sounds and movement. Parcels slap and hit; motor omnibuses graze the kerb; the blare of a whole brass band in full tongue dwindles to a thin reed of sound.

Buses, vans, cars, barrows stream past like the fragments of a picture puzzle; a white arm rises; the puzzle runs thick, coagulates, stops; the white arm sinks, and away it streams again, streaked, twisted, higgledy-piggledy, in perpetual race and disorder. The puzzle never fits itself together, however long we look.

On the banks of this river of turning wheels our modern aristocrats have built palaces just as in ancient days the Dukes of Somerset and Northumberland, the Earls of Dorset and Salisbury lined the Strand with their stately mansions. The different houses of the great firms testify to the courage, initiative, the audacity of their creators much as the great houses of Cavendish and Percy testify to such qualities in some faraway shire. From the loins of our merchants will spring the Cavendishes and Percys of the future. Indeed, the great Lords of Oxford Street are as magnanimous as any Duke or Earl who scattered gold or doled out loaves to the poor at his gates. Only their largesse takes a different form. It takes the form of excitement, of display, of entertainment, of windows lit up by night, of banners flaunting by day. They give us the latest news for nothing. Music streams from their banqueting rooms free. You need not spend more than one and eleven three to enjoy all the shelter that high and airy halls provide; and the soft pile of carpets, and the luxury of lifts, and the glow of fabrics, and carpets and silver. Percy and Cavendish could give no more. These gifts of course have an object – to entice the shilling and 11 pennies as freely from our pockets as possible; but the Percys and the Cavendishes were not munificent either without hope of some return, whether it was a dedication from a poet or a vote from a farmer. And both the old lords and the new added considerably to the decoration and entertainment of human life.

But it cannot be denied that these Oxford Street palaces are rather flimsy abodes – perhaps grounds rather than dwelling places. One is conscious that one is walking on a strip of wood laid upon steel girders, and that the outer wall, for all its florid ornamentation, is only thick enough to withstand the force of the wind. A vigorous prod with an umbrella point might well inflict irreparable damage upon the fabric. Many a country cottage built to house farmer or miller when Queen Elizabeth was on the throne will live to see these palaces fall into the dust. The old cottage walls, with their oak beams and their layers of honest brick soundly cemented together still put up a stout resistance to the drills and bores that attempt to introduce the modern blessing of electricity. But any day of the week one may see Oxford Street vanishing at the tap of a workman's pick as he stands perilously balanced on a dusty pinnacle knocking down walls and façades as lightly as if they were made of cardboard and sugar icing.

And again the moralists point the finger of scorn. For such thinness, such papery stone and powdery brick reflect, they say, the levity, the ostentation, the haste and irresponsibility of our age. Yet perhaps they are as much out in their scorn as we should be if we asked of the lily that it should be cast in bronze, or of the daisy that it should have petals of imperishable enamel. The charm of modern London is that it is not built to last; it is built to pass. Its glassiness, its transparency, its surging waves of coloured plaster give a different pleasure and achieve a different end from that which was desired and attempted by the old build-ers and their patrons, the nobility of England. Their pride required the illusion of permanence. Ours, on the contrary, seems to delight in proving that we can make stone and brick as

transitory as our own desires. We do not build for our descend-
ants, who may live up in the clouds or down in the earth, but
for ourselves and our own needs. We knock down and rebuild
as we expect to be knocked down and rebuilt. It is an impulse
that makes for creation and fertility. Discovery is stimulated and
invention on the alert.

The palaces of Oxford Street ignore what seemed good to the
Greeks, to the Elizabethan, to the 18th-century nobleman; they
are overwhelmingly conscious that unless they can devise an
architecture that shows off the dressing case, the Paris frock, the
cheap stockings, and the jar of bath salts to perfection, their
palaces, their mansions and motor cars and the little villas out at
Croydon and Surbiton where their shop assistants live, not so
badly after all, with a gramophone and wireless, and money to
spend at the movies – all this will be swept to ruin. Hence they
stretch stone fantastically; crush together in one wild confusion
the styles of Greece, Egypt, Italy, America; and boldly attempt
an air of lavishness, opulence, in their effort to persuade the
multitude that here unending beauty, ever fresh, ever new, very
cheap and within the reach of everybody, bubbles up every day
of the week from an inexhaustible well. The mere thought of
age, of solidity, of lasting for ever is abhorrent to Oxford Street.

Therefore if the moralist chooses to take his afternoon walk
along this particular thoroughfare, he must tune his strain so that
it receives into it some queer, incongruous voices. Above the
racket of van and omnibus we can hear them crying. God
knows, says the man who sells tortoises, that my arm aches; my
chance of selling a tortoise is small; but courage! there may come
along a buyer; my bed tonight depends on it; so on I must go, as
slowly as the police allow, wheeling tortoises down Oxford
Street from dawn till dusk. True, says the great merchant, I am
not thinking of educating the mass to a higher standard of
aesthetic sensibility. It taxes all my wits to think how I can display
my goods with the minimum of waste and the maximum of

effectiveness. Green dragons on the top of Corinthian columns may help; let us try. I grant, says the middle-class woman, that I linger and look and barter and cheapen and turn over basket after basket of remnants hour by hour. My eyes glisten unseemlily I know, and I grab and pounce with disgusting greed. But my husband is a small clerk in a bank; I have only £15 a year to dress on; so here I come, to linger and loiter and look, if I can, as well dressed as my neighbours. I am a thief, says a woman of that persuasion, and a lady of easy virtue into the bargain. But it takes pluck to snatch a bag from a counter when a customer is not looking; and it may contain only spectacles and old bus tickets after all. So here goes! A thousand such voices are always crying aloud in Oxford Street. All are tense, all are real, all are urged out of their speakers by the pressure of making a living, finding a bed, somehow keeping afloat on the bounding, careless, remorseless tide of the street. And even a moralist, who is, one must suppose, since he can spend the afternoon dreaming, a man with a balance in the bank – even a moralist must allow that this gaudy, bustling, vulgar street reminds us that life is a struggle; that all building is perishable; that all display is vanity; from which we may conclude – but until some adroit shopkeeper has caught on to the idea and opened cells for solitary thinkers hung with green plush and provided with automatic glow-worms and a sprinkling of genuine death's head moths to induce thought and reflection, it is vain to try to come to a conclusion in Oxford Street.

Christmas Plum Pudding

Mrs Beeton

Ingredients: 1 ½ lb of raisins, ½ lb of currants, ¾ lb of breadcrumbs, ½ lb of mixed peel, ¾ lb of suet, 8 eggs, 1 wineglassful of brandy

Mode: Stone and cut the raisins in halves, but do not chop them; wash, pick and dry the currants, and mince the suet finely; cut the candied peel into thin slices, and grate down the bread into fine crumbs.

When all these dry ingredients are prepared, mix them well together; then moisten the mixture with the eggs, which should be well beaten, and the brandy; stir well, that everything may be very thoroughly blended, and *press* the pudding into a buttered mould; tie it down tightly with a floured cloth, and boil for five or six hours. It may be boiled in a cloth without a mould, and will require the same time allowed for cooking.

As Christmas puddings are usually made a few days before they are required for table, when the pudding is taken out of the pot, hang it up immediately, and put a plate or saucer underneath to catch the water that may drain from it. The day it is to be eaten, plunge it into boiling water, and keep it boiling for at least two hours; then turn it out of the mould and serve with brandy sauce. On Christmas Day a sprig of holly is usually placed in the middle of the pudding and about a wineglassful of brandy poured round it, which at the moment of serving, is lighted and the pudding thus brought to the table encircled in flame.

Average cost: 4s *Sufficient* for a quart mould for seven or eight persons. Seasonable on the 25th December, and on various festive occasions till March.

Mole's Christmas

from *The Wind in the Willows*, Kenneth Grahame

The Rat paid no heed to his doleful self-reproaches. He was running here and there, opening doors, inspecting rooms and cupboards, and lighting lamps and candles and sticking them up everywhere. 'What a capital little house this is!' he called out cheerily. 'So compact! So well planned! Everything here and everything in its place! We'll make a jolly night of it. The first thing we want is a good fire; I'll see to that – I always know where to find things. So this is the parlour? Splendid! Your own idea, those little sleeping-bunks in the wall? Capital! Now, I'll fetch the wood and the coals, and you get a duster, Mole – you'll find one in the drawer of the kitchen table – and try and smarten things up a bit. Bustle about, old chap!'

Encouraged by his inspiriting companion, the Mole roused himself and dusted and polished with energy and heartiness, while the Rat, running to and fro with armfuls of fuel, soon had a cheerful blaze roaring up the chimney. He hailed the Mole to come and warm himself; but Mole promptly had another fit of the blues, dropping down on a couch in dark despair and burying his face in his duster.

'Rat,' he moaned, 'how about your supper, you poor, cold, hungry, weary animal? I've nothing to give you – nothing – not a crumb!'

'What a fellow you are for giving in!' said the Rat reproachfully. 'Why, only just now I saw a sardine-opener on the kitchen dresser, quite distinctly; and everybody knows that means there are sardines about somewhere in the neighbourhood. Rouse yourself! Pull yourself together, and come with me and forage.'

They went and foraged accordingly, hunting through every cupboard and turning out every drawer. The result was not so very depressing after all, though of course it might have been better; a tin of sardines – a box of captain's biscuits, nearly full – and a German sausage encased in silver paper.

'There's a banquet for you!' observed the Rat, as he arranged the table. 'I know some animals who would give their ears to be sitting down to supper with us tonight!'

'No bread!' groaned the Mole dolorously; 'no butter, no—'

'No *pâté de foie gras*, no champagne!' continued the Rat, grinning. 'And that reminds me – what's that little door at the end of the passage? Your cellar, of course! Every luxury in this house! Just you wait a minute.'

He made for the cellar-door, and presently reappeared, somewhat dusty, with a bottle of beer in each paw and another under each arm. 'Self-indulgent beggar you seem to be, Mole,' he observed. 'Deny yourself nothing. This is really the jolliest little place I ever was in. Now, wherever did you pick up those prints? Make the place look so home-like, they do. No wonder you're so fond of it, Mole. Tell us all about it, and how you came to make it what it is.'

Then, while the Rat busied himself fetching plates, and knives and forks, and mustard which he mixed in an egg-cup, the Mole, his bosom still heaving with the stress of his recent emotion, related – somewhat shyly at first, but with more freedom as he warmed to his subject – how this was planned, and how that was thought out, and how this was got through a windfall from an aunt, and that was a wonderful find and a bargain, and this other thing was bought out of laborious savings and a certain amount of 'going without'. His spirits finally quite restored, he must needs go and caress his possessions, and take a lamp and show off their points to his visitor and expatiate on them, quite forgetful of the supper they both so much needed; Rat, who was desperately hungry but strove to conceal it, nodding seriously, examining with a puckered brow, and saying, 'wonderful', and 'most remarkable', at intervals, when the chance for an observation was given him.

At last the Rat succeeded in decoying him to the table, and had just got seriously to work with the sardine-opener when sounds were heard from the fore-court without – sounds like the scuffling of small feet in the gravel and a confused murmur of tiny voices, while broken sentences reached them – 'Now, all in a line – hold the lantern up a bit, Tommy – clear your throats first – no coughing after I say one, two, three. – Where's young Bill? – Here, come on, do, we're all a-waiting—'

'What's up?' inquired the Rat, pausing in his labours.

'I think it must be the field-mice,' replied the Mole, with a touch of pride in his manner. 'They go round carol-singing regularly at this time of the year. They're quite an institution in these parts. And they never pass me over – they come to Mole End last of all; and I used to give them hot drinks, and supper too sometimes, when I could afford it. It will be like old times to hear them again.'

'Let's have a look at them!' cried the Rat, jumping up and running to the door.

It was a pretty sight, and a seasonable one, that met their eyes when they flung the door open. In the fore-court, lit by the dim rays of a horn lantern, some eight or ten little field mice stood in a semicircle, red worsted comforters round their throats, their fore-paws thrust deep into their pockets, their feet jigging for warmth. With bright beady eyes they glanced shyly at each other, sniggering a little, sniffing and applying coat-sleeves a good deal. As the door opened, one of the elder ones that carried the lantern was just saying, 'Now then, one, two, three!' and forthwith their shrill little voices uprose on the air, singing one of the old-time carols that their forefathers composed in fields that were fallow and held by frost, or when snow-bound in chimney corners, and handed down to be sung in the miry street to lamp-lit windows at Yule-time.

CAROL

Villagers all, this frosty tide,
Let your doors swing open wide,
Though wind may follow, and snow beside,
Yet draw us in by your fire to bide;
Joy shall be yours in the morning!

Here we stand in the cold and the sleet,
Blowing fingers and stamping feet,
Come from far away you to greet –
You by the fire and we in the street –
Bidding you joy in the morning!

For ere one half of the night was gone,
Sudden a star has led us on,
Raining bliss and benison –
Bliss tomorrow and more anon,
Joy for every morning!

Goodman Joseph toiled through the snow –
Saw the star o'er a stable low;
Mary she might not further go –
Welcome thatch, and litter below!
Joy was hers in the morning!

And then they heard the angels tell
'Who were the first to cry Nowell?
Animals all, as it befell,
In the stable where they did dwell!
Joy shall be theirs in the morning!'

The Christmas Decorations

from *Character and Comedy*, E. V. Lucas

The Rev Lawrence Lidbetter to his curate, the Rev Arthur Starling.
DEAR Starling, – I am sorry to appear to be running away at this busy season, but a sudden call to London on business leaves me no alternative. I shall be back on Christmas Eve for certain, perhaps before. You must keep an eye on the decorations, and see that none of our helpers get out of hand. I have serious doubts as to Miss Green. –

Yours, L. L.

Mrs Clibborn to the Rev Lawrence Lidbetter.
DEAR Rector, – I think we have got over the difficulty which we were talking of – Mr Lulham's red hair and the discord it would make with the crimson decorations. Maggie and Popsy and I have been working like slaves, and have put up a beautiful and effectual screen of evergreen which completely obliterates the keyboard and organist. I think you will be delighted. Mr Starling approves most cordially. – Yours sincerely,

MARY CLIBBORN.

Miss Pitt to the Rev Lawrence Lidbetter.
MY dear Mr Lidbetter, – We are all so sorry you have been called away, a strong guiding hand being never more needed. You will remember that it was arranged that I should have sole charge of the memorial window to Colonel Soper – we settled it just outside the Post Office on the morning that poor Blades was kicked by the Doctor's pony. Well, Miss Lockie now says that

Colonel Soper's window belongs to her, and she makes it impossible for me to do anything. I must implore you to write to her putting it right, or the decorations will be ruined. Mr Starling is kind, but quite useless. – Yours sincerely,

VIRGINIA PITT.

Miss Lockie to the Rev Lawrence Lidbetter.

MY dear Mr Lidbetter, – I am sorry to have to trouble you in your enforced rest, but the interests of the church must not be neglected, and you ought to know that Miss Pitt not only insists that the decoration of Colonel Soper's window was entrusted to her, but prevents me carrying it out. If you recollect, it was during tea at Mrs Millstone's that it was arranged that I should be responsible for this window. A telegram to Miss Pitt would put the matter right at once. Dear Mr Starling is always so nice, but he does so lack firmness. – Yours sincerely,

MABEL LOCKIE.

Mrs St John to the Rev Lawrence Lidbetter.

DEAR Rector, – I wish you would let Miss Green have a line about the decoration of the pulpit. It is no use any of us saying anything to her since she went to the Slade School and acquired artistic notions, but a word from you would work wonders. What we all feel is that the pulpit should be bright and gay, with some cheerful texts on it, a suitable setting for you and your helpful Christmas sermon, but Miss Green's idea is to drape it entirely in black muslin and purple, like a lying in state. One can do wonders with a little cotton-wool and a few yards of Turkey twill, but she will not understand this. How with all her *nouveau art* ideas she got permission to decorate the pulpit at all I cannot think, but there it is, and the sooner she is stopped the better. Poor Mr Starling drops all the hints he can, but she disregards them all. – Yours sincerely,

CHARLOTTE ST JOHN.

Miss Olive Green to the Rev Lawrence Lidbetter.

DEAR Mr Lidbetter, – I am sure you will like the pulpit. I am giving it the most careful thought, and there is every promise of a scheme of austere beauty, grave and solemn and yet just touched with a note of happier fulfilment. For the most part you will find the decorations quite conventional – holly and evergreens, the old terrible cotton-wool snow on crimson background. But I am certain that you will experience a thrill of satisfied surprise when your eyes alight upon the simple gravity of the pulpit's drapery and its flowing sensuous lines. It is so kind of you to give me this opportunity to realise some of my artistic self. Poor Mr Starling, who is entirely Victorian in his views of art, has been talking to me about gay colours, but my work is done for *you* and the few who can *understand*. – Yours sincerely,

OLIVE GREEN.

Mrs Millstone to the Rev Lawrence Lidbetter.

DEAR Rector, – Just a line to tell you of a delightful device I have hit upon for the decorations. Cotton-wool, of course, makes excellent snow, and rice is sometimes used, on gum, to suggest winter too. But I have discovered that the most perfect illusion of a white rime can be obtained by wetting the leaves and then sprinkling flour on them. I am going to get all the others to let me finish off everything like that on Christmas Eve (like varnishing-day at the Academy, my husband says), when it will all be fresh for Sunday. Mr Starling who is proving himself such a dear, is delighted with the scheme. I hope you are well in that dreadful foggy city. – Yours sincerely,

ADA MILLSTONE.

Mrs Hobbs, charwoman, to the Rev Lawrence Lidbetter.

HONOURED Sir, – I am writing to you because Hobbs and me dispare of getting any justice from the so called ladies who have been turning the holy church of St Michael and all Angels into a Covent Garden market. To sweep up all holly and green stuff I don't mind, because I have heard you say year after year that we should all do our best at Christmas to help each other. I always hold that charity and kindness are more than rubys, but when it comes to flour I say no. If you would believe it, Mrs Millstone is first watering the holly and the lorrel to make it wet, and then sprinkling flour on it to look like hore frost, and the mess is something dreadful, all over the cushions and carpet. To sweep up ordinery dust I don't mind, more particularly as it is my paid work and bounden duty; but unless it is made worth my while Hobbs says I must say no. We draw the line at sweeping up dough. Mr Starling is very kind, but as Hobbs says you are the founting head. – Awaiting a reply, I am, your humble servant,

MARTHA HOBBS.

Mrs Vansittart to the Rev Lawrence Lidbetter.

DEAR Rector, – If I am late with the north windows you must understand that it is not my fault, but Pedder's. He has suddenly and most mysteriously adopted an attitude of hostility to his employers (quite in the way one has heard of gardeners doing), and nothing will induce him to cut me any evergreens, which he says he cannot spare. The result is that poor Horace and Mr Starling have to go out with lanterns after Pedder has left the garden, and cut what they can and convey it to the church by stealth. I think we shall manage fairly well, but thought you had better know in case the result is not equal to your anticipation. – Yours sincerely,

GRACE VANSITTART.

Mr Lulham, organist, to the Rev Lawrence Lidbetter.

DEAR Sir, – I shall be glad to have a line from you authorising me to insist upon the removal of a large screen of evergreens which Mrs Clibborn and her daughters have erected by the organ. There seems to be an idea that the organ is unsightly, although we have had no complaints hitherto, and the effect of this barrier will be to interfere very seriously with the choral part of the service. Mr Starling sympathises with me, but has not taken any steps. – Believe me, yours faithfully,

WALTER LULHAM.

The Rev Lawrence Lidbetter to Mrs Lidbetter.

MY Dearest Harriet, – I am having, as I expected, an awful time with the decorations, and I send you a batch of letters and leave the situation to you. Miss Pitt had better keep the Soper window. Give the Lockie girl one of the autograph copies of my *Narrow Path*, with a reference underneath my name to the chapter on self-sacrifice, and tell her how sorry I am that there has been a misunderstanding. Mrs Hobbs must have an extra half-crown, and the flouring must be discreetly discouraged – on the ground of waste of food material. Assure Lulham that there shall be no barrier, and then tell Mrs Clibborn that the organist has been given a pledge that nothing should intervene between his music and the congregation. I am dining with the Lawsons tonight,

and we go afterwards to the *Tempest*, I think. – Your
devoted,

A Song Against Bores

from *The Commonplace Book of R. Hill*

Make we mery bothe more and lasse,
For now is the time of Cristemas!

Lett no man cum into this hall,
Grome, page, nor yet marshall,
But that sum sport he bring with all;
For now is the time of Cristemas!

If that he say he can not sing,
Some oder sport then lett him bring,
That it may please at this festing;
For now is the time of Cristemas!

If he say he can nought do,
Then for my love aske him no mo,
But to the stokkes then let him go;
For now is the time of Cristemas!

A Fenland Carol

Rudyard Kipling

Our Lord who did the Ox command
To kneel to Judah's King,
He binds His frost upon the land
To ripen it for Spring –
To ripen it for Spring, good sirs,
According to His Word.
Which well must be, as ye can see –
And who shall judge the Lord?

When we poor Fenmen skate the ice
Or shiver on the Wold,
We hear the cry of a single tree
That breaks her heart in the cold –
That breaks her heart in the cold, good sirs
And rendeth by the board,
Which well must be, as ye can see –
And who shall judge the Lord?

Her wood is crazed and little worth
Excepting as to burn,
That we may warm and make our mirth
Until the Spring return –
Until the Spring return, good sirs,
When Christians walk abroad;
Which well must be, as ye can see –
And who shall judge the Lord?

God Bless the Master of this house,
And all who sleep therein!
And guard the Fens from pirate folk,
And keep us all from sin,
To walk in honesty, good sirs,
Of thought and deed and word!
Which shall befriend our latter end –
And who shall judge the Lord?

The Anticipation of Christmas

from *Essays in London*, Henry James

There is still something that recalls to me the enchantment of children – the anticipation of Christmas, the delight of a holiday walk – in the way the shop-fronts shine into the fog. It makes each of them seem a little world of light and warmth, and I can still waste time in looking at them with dirty Bloomsbury on one side and dirtier Soho on the other. There are winter effects, not intrinsically sweet, it would appear, which somehow, in absence, touch the chords of memory and even the fount of tears: as for instance the front of the British Museum on a black afternoon, or the portico, when the weather is vile, of one of the big square clubs in Pall Mall. I can give no adequate account of the subtle poetry of such reminiscences; it depends upon associations of which we have often lost the thread. The wide colonnade of the Museum, its symmetrical wings, the high iron fence in its granite setting, the sense of the misty halls within, where all the treasures lie – these things loom patiently through atmospheric layers which instead of making them dreary impart to them something of a cheer of red lights in a storm. I think the romance of a winter afternoon in London arises partly from the fact that, when it is not altogether smothered, the general lamplight takes this hue of hospitality. Such is the colour of the interior glow of clubs in Pall Mall, which I positively like best when the fog loiters upon their monumental staircases.

A Child's Christmas in Wales

Dylan Thomas

We returned home through the poor streets where only a few children fumbled with bare red fingers in the wheel-rutted snow and cat-called after us, their voices fading away, as we trudged uphill, into the cries of the dock birds and the hooting of ships out in the whirling bay. And then, at tea the recovered Uncles would be jolly; and the ice cake loomed in the centre of the table like a marble grave. Auntie Hannah laced her tea with rum, because it was only once a year.

Bring out the tall tales now that we told by the fire as the gaslight bubbled like a diver. Ghosts whooed like owls in the long nights when I dared not look over my shoulder; animals lurked in the cubbyhole under the stairs and the gas meter ticked. And I remember that we went singing carols once, when there wasn't the shaving of a moon to light the flying streets. At the end of a long road was a drive that led to a large house, and we stumbled up the darkness of the drive that night, each one of us afraid, each one holding a stone in his hand in case, and all of us too brave to say a word. The wind through the trees made noises as of old and unpleasant and maybe webfooted men wheezing in caves. We reached the black bulk of the house.

'What shall we give them? "Hark the Herald"?'

'No,' Jack said, '"Good King Wencelas". I'll count three.' One, two three, and we began to sing, our voices high and seemingly distant in the snow-felted darkness round the house that was occupied by nobody we knew. We stood close together, near the dark door.

'*Good King Wencelas looked out*
On the Feast of Stephen' . . .

And then a small, dry voice, like the voice of someone who has not spoken for a long time, joined our singing: a small, dry, eggshell voice from the other side of the door: a small dry voice through the keyhole. And when we stopped running we were outside our house; the front room was lovely; balloons floated under the hot-water-bottle-gulping gas; everything was good again and shone over the town.

'Perhaps it was a ghost,' Jim said.

'Perhaps it was trolls,' Dan said, who was always reading.

'Let's go in and see if there's any jelly left,' Jack said. And we did that.

A Christmas Carpet Trip

from *The Pheonix and the Carpet,* Edith Nesbit

'Well, look here,' said Anthea. 'You know there's something about Christmas that makes you want to be good – however little you wish it at other times. Couldn't we wish the carpet to take us some-where where we should have the chance to do some good and kind action? It would be an adventure just the same,' she pleaded.

'I don't mind,' said Cyril. 'We shan't know where we're going, and that'll be exciting. No one knows what'll happen. We'd best put on our outers in case—'

'We might rescue a traveller buried in the snow, like St

Bernard dogs, with barrels round our necks,' said Jane, beginning to be interested.

'Or we might arrive just in time to witness a will being signed
– more tea, please,' said Robert 'and we should see the old man
hide it away in the secret cupboard; and then, after long years,
when the rightful heir was in despair, we should lead him to the
hidden panel and—'

'Yes,' interrupted Anthea, 'or we might be taken to some
freezing garret in a German town, where a poor little pale, sick
child—'

'We haven't any German money,' interrupted Cyril, 'so *that's* no
go. What I should like would be getting into the middle of a war
and getting hold of secret intelligence and taking it to the general,
and he would make me a lieutenant, or a scout, or a hussar.'

When breakfast was cleared away, Anthea swept the carpet, and
the children sat down on it, together with the Phoenix, who had
been especially invited, as a Christmas treat, to come with them
and witness the good and kind action they were about to do.

Four children and one bird were ready, and the wish was
wished.

Every one closed its eyes, so as to feel the topsy-turvy swirl of
the carpet's movement as little as possible.

[. . .]

The passage was long, and there were arches and steps and
turnings and dark alcoves that the girls did not much like passing.
The passage ended in a flight of steps. Robert went up them.

Suddenly he staggered heavily back on to the following feet
of Jane, and everybody screamed, 'Oh! what is it?'

'I've only bashed my head in,' said Robert, when he had
groaned for some time; 'that's all. Don't mention it; I like it. The
stairs just go right slap into the ceiling, and it's a stone ceiling.
You can't do good and kind actions underneath a paving-stone.'

'Stairs aren't made to lead just to paving-stones as a general
rule,' said the Phoenix. 'Put your shoulder to the wheel.'

'There isn't any wheel,' said the injured Robert, still rubbing his head.

But Cyril had pushed past him to the top stair, and was already shoving his hardest against the stone above. Of course, it did not give in the least.

'If it's a trap-door—' said Cyril. And he stopped shoving and began to feel about with his hands.

'Yes, there is a bolt. I can't move it.'

By a happy chance Cyril had in his pocket the oil-can of his father's bicycle; he put the carpet down at the foot of the stairs, and he lay on his back, with his head on the top step and his feet straggling down among his young relations, and he oiled the bolt till the drops of rust and oil fell down on his face. One even went into his mouth – open, as he panted with the exertion of keeping up this unnatural position. Then he tried again, but still the bolt would not move. So now he tied his handkerchief – the one with the bacon fat and marmalade on it – to the bolt, and Robert's handkerchief to that, in a reef knot, which cannot come undone however much you pull, and, indeed, gets tighter and tighter the more you pull it. This must not be confused with a granny knot, which comes undone if you look at it. And then he and Robert pulled, and the girls put their arms round their brothers and pulled too, and suddenly the bolt gave way with a rusty scrunch, and they all rolled together to the bottom of the stairs – all but the Phoenix, which had taken to its wings when the pulling began.

Nobody was hurt much, because the rolled-up carpet broke their fall; and now, indeed, the shoulders of the boys were used to some purpose, for the stone allowed them to heave it up. They felt it give; dust fell freely on them.

'Now, then,' cried Robert, forgetting his head and his temper, 'push all together. One, two, three!'

The stone was heaved up. It swung up on a creaking, unwilling hinge, and showed a growing oblong of dazzling daylight; and it fell back with a bang against something that kept it upright. Every one climbed out, but there was not room for every one to stand comfortably in the little paved house where they found themselves, so when the Phoenix had fluttered up from the darkness they let the stone down, and it closed like a trap-door, as indeed it was.

You can have no idea how dusty and dirty the children were. Fortunately there was no one to see them but each other. The place they were in was a little shrine, built on the side of a road that went winding up through yellow-green fields to the topless tower. Below them were fields and orchards, all bare boughs and brown furrows, and little houses and gardens. The shrine was a kind of tiny chapel with no front wall – just a place for people to stop and rest in and wish to be good. So the Phoenix told them. There was an image that had once been brightly coloured, but the rain and snow had beaten in through the open front of the shrine, and the poor image was dull and weather-stained. Under it was written: 'St Jean de Luz. *Priez pour nous.*' It was a sad little place, very neglected and lonely, and yet it was nice, Anthea thought, that poor travellers should come to this little rest-house in the hurry and worry of their journeyings and be quiet for a few minutes, and think about being good. The thought of St Jean de Luz – who had, no doubt, in his time, been very good and kind – made Anthea want more than ever to do something kind and good.

'Tell us,' she said to the Phoenix, 'what is the good and kind action the carpet brought us here to do?'

'I think it would be kind to find the owners of the treasure and tell them about it,' said Cyril.

'And give it them *all?*' said Jane.

'Yes. But whose is it?'

'I should go to the first house and ask the name of the owner of the castle,' said the golden bird, and really the idea seemed a good one.

[. . .]

There was a wood fire, very small and very bright, on the hearth – neat little logs laid on brass fire-dogs. Some portraits of powdered ladies and gentlemen hung in oval frames on the pale walls. There were silver candlesticks on the mantelpiece, and there were chairs and a table, very slim and polite, with slender legs. The room was extremely bare, but with a bright foreign bareness that was very cheerful, in an odd way of its own. At the end of the polished table a very unEnglish little boy sat on a footstool in a high-backed, uncomfortable-looking chair. He wore black velvet, and the kind of collar – all frills and lacey – that Robert would rather have died than wear; but then the little French boy was much younger than Robert.

'Oh, how pretty!' said every one. But no one meant the little French boy, with the velvety short knickerbockers and the velvety short hair.

What every one admired was a little, little Christmas tree, very green, and standing in a very red little flowerpot, and hung round with very bright little things made of tinsel and coloured paper. There were tiny candles on the tree, but they were not lighted yet.

'But yes – is it not that it is genteel?' said the lady. 'Sit down you then, and let us see.'

The children sat down in a row on the stiff chairs against the wall, and the lady lighted a long, slim red taper at the wood flame, and then she drew the curtains and lit the little candles, and when they were all lighted the little French boy suddenly shouted, '*Bravo, ma tante! Oh, que c'est gentil*,' and the English children shouted 'Hooray!'

Then there was a struggle in the breast of Robert, and out fluttered the Phoenix – spread his gold wings, flew to the top of the Christmas tree, and perched there.

'Ah! catch it, then,' cried the lady; 'it will itself burn – your genteel parrakeet!'

'It won't,' said Robert, 'thank you.'

And the little French boy clapped his clean and tidy hands; but the lady was so anxious that the Phoenix fluttered down and walked up and down on the shiny walnut-wood table.

'Is it that it talks?' asked the lady.

And the Phoenix replied in excellent French. It said, '*Parfaitement, madame!*'

'Oh, the pretty parrakeet,' said the lady. 'Can it say still of other things?'

And the Phoenix replied, this time in English, 'Why are you sad so near Christmas-time?'

The children looked at it with one gasp of horror and surprise, for the youngest of them knew that it is far from manners to notice that strangers have been crying, and much worse to ask them the reason of their tears. And, of course, the lady began to cry again, very much indeed, after calling the Phoenix a bird without a heart; and she could not find her handkerchief, so Anthea offered hers, which was still very damp and no use at all. She also hugged the lady, and this seemed to be of more use than the handkerchief, so that presently the lady stopped crying, and found her own handkerchief and dried her eyes, and called Anthea a cherished angel.

'I am sorry we came just when you were so sad,' said Anthea, 'but we really only wanted to ask you whose that castle is on the hill.'

'Oh, my little angel,' said the poor lady, sniffing, 'today and for hundreds of years the castle is to us, to our family. Tomorrow it must that I sell it to some strangers – and my little Henri, who ignores all, he will not have never the lands paternal. But what will you? His father, my brother – Mr the Marquis – has spent much of money, and it the must, despite the sentiments of familial respect, that I admit that my sainted father he also –'

'How would you feel if you found a lot of money – hundreds and thousands of gold pieces?' asked Cyril.

The lady smiled sadly.

'Ah! one has already recounted to you the legend?' she said. 'It is true that one says that it is long time; oh! but long time, one of our ancestors has hid a treasure – of gold, and of gold, and of gold – enough to enrich my little Henri for the life. But all that, my children, it is but the accounts of fays –'

'She means fairy stories,' whispered the Phoenix to Robert. 'Tell her what you have found.'

So Robert told, while Anthea and Jane hugged the lady for fear she should faint for joy, like people in books, and they hugged her with the earnest, joyous hugs of unselfish delight.

'It's no use explaining how we got in,' said Robert, when he had told of the finding of the treasure, 'because you would find it a little difficult to understand, and much more difficult to believe. But we can show you where the gold is and help you to fetch it away.'

The lady looked doubtfully at Robert as she absently returned the hugs of the girls.

'No, he's not making it up,' said Anthea; 'it's true, true, TRUE! – and we are so glad.'

'You would not be capable to torment an old woman?' she said; 'and it is not possible that it be a dream.'

'It really is true,' said Cyril; 'and I congratulate you very much.'

At Windsor Castle

from *Queen Victoria's Personal Journals*, 1850

24th December 1850. The frost gone, & a raw dull morning. Albert out shooting, & I, walking with the Children. We walked out in the afternoon, & found it raw & damp. We began, by giving our presents to poor Lady Lyttelton, a bracelet containing the portraits of our five younger Children, & 2 prints of the Children. Then gave presents to our personal servants &c, & were busy arranging the tables.

At a little after 6 we all assembled & my beloved Albert first took me to my tree & table, covered by such numberless gifts, really too much, too magnificent. I am delighted with the really splendid picture in watercolours by Corbauld, representing the famous scene at the Coronation in 'Le Prophète' – & a very pretty oil painting of 'Faith' represented by a female figure & 2 angels, by Mrs Richards, also a fine oil painting of 'L'Allegro' & 'Il Penseroso', by Hurseley. The one present from dearest Albert, which is of infinite value to me, is a miniature of my beloved Louise in a clasp to a bracelet in dull, deepish blue enamel, with a black cross, the cypher & stars in diamonds, all, dear Albert's own design & very lovely.

I also received charming gifts from dear Mama. The 3 girls all worked me something. The 7 children were then taken to their tree, jumping & shouting with joy over their toys & other presents; the Boys could think of nothing but the swords we had given them, & Bertie of some armour, which however he complained, pinched him!

Mama had her tree & table in the same room, & Albert his, in the 3rd last room. Amongst my gifts was a painting by Landseer, as a pendant to his 'Lassie' – a Highlander in a snowstorm 'on the Hull', with a dead eagle in one hand, & a dog near him. The colouring is beautiful, & the whole thing is a 'chef d'oeuvre'.

Dear Albert was kindly pleased with everything, but I felt it was so poor in comparison to what he had given me. At 7, we gave the Ladies & Gentlemen their tree and gifts, & then showed them our things. Mama, &c to dinner, Lord Camoys sitting next to me, having just come into waiting . . .

25th December. The return of this blessed season must always fill one with gratitude & with the deepest devotion to Our Lord &

Saviour! May God grant that we may all see many happy returns of this great Festival. We walked with the Children to the Kennels, where I gave the good little McDonalds toys & stuff for dresses. The day was beautiful but almost too mild for Christmas! Service at 11. Went several times to look at my beautiful presents. The trees were lit up in the evening, & the Children were all playing about so happily. Mama, &c – the Phippses, Mrs Grey, Mrs Bouverie, Gen. Wemyss, Mr Wellesley, Mr Birch, Mr Glover & Meyer, dined. The 2 little girls & Affie appeared during dinner, & the others, after.

26th December. A dull & raw morning. Albert, out hunting, & I, walking with the Children. The little McDonalds & little Flemmings (to whom I had also given something) were much delighted with their Xmas presents, when we went in to see them. Rode afterwards in the Riding School on 'Hammon' & 'Ronald'. A rainy afternoon, but got out for a short walk. At ½ p. 6 the Children performed their Charade, the same as last year, but without the dancing & the last scene. Some of the scenery from our Theatre was made use of, & the whole looked very nice. The Children were particularly well got up, but did not act as well, being rather absent. Bertie spoke the best. They each recited a piece of poetry, and Bertie the 7 Ages, by Shakespeare, which he did remarkably well. The performance ended with a little dance with the Phipps Children, who had come to see the Charade. Bessy Douro, Caroline Cavendish, Stockmar, & Clark were also there. Mama, &c to dinner.

CHRISTMAS EVE

A Further Thought

G. K. Chesterton

The child who doubts about Santa Claus has insomnia. The child who believes has a good night's rest.

Country-house Christmas

from *English Hours*, Henry James

I left town a short time before Christmas and went to spend the festive season in the North, in a part of the country with which I was acquainted. It was quite possible to absent one's self from London without a sense of sacrifice, for the charms of the capital during the last several weeks have been obscured by peculiarly vile weather. It is of course a very old story that London is foggy, and this simple statement raises no blush of face on the face of Nature as we see it here. But there are fogs and fogs, and the folds of the black mantle have been during the present winter intolerably thick. The thickness that draws down and absorbs the smoke of the house-tops, causes it to hang about the streets in impenetrable density, forces it into one's eyes and down one's throat, so that one is half blinded and quite sickened – this form of the particular plague has been too much more frequent than usual. Just before Christmas, too, there was a heavy snowstorm, and even a tolerably light fall of snow has London quite at its mercy. The emblem of purity is almost immediately converted into a sticky, lead-coloured mush, the cabs skulk out of sight or take up their situations before the lurid windows of a public house, which glares through the sleety darkness at the desperate wayfarer with an air of vulgar bravado. For recovery of one's nervous balance the only course was flight – flight to the country and the confinement of one's vision to the large area of one of those admirable homes which at this season overflow with hospitality and good cheer. By this means the readjustment is effectually brought about – these are conditions that you cordially appreciate.

Of all the great things that the English have invented and made a part of the credit of the national character, the most perfect, the most characteristic, the one they have mastered most completely in all its details, so that it has become a compendious illustration of their social genius and their manners, is the well-appointed, well-administered, well-filled country-house. The grateful stranger makes these reflections – and others besides – as he wanders about in the beautiful library for such a small dwelling, of an inclement winter afternoon, just at the hour when six o'clock tea is impending. Such a place and such a time abound in agreeable episodes; but I suspect that the episode from which, a fortnight ago, I received the most ineffaceable impression was but indirectly connected with the charms of a luxurious fireside. The country I speak of was a populous manufacturing region, full of tall chimneys and of an air that is gray and gritty. A lady had made a present of a Christmas tree to the children of a workhouse, and she invited me to go with her and assist at the distribution of the toys. There was a drive through the early dusk of a very cold Christmas Eve, followed by the drawing up of a lamp-lit brougham in the snowy quadrangle of a grim-looking charitable institution. I had never been in an English workhouse before, and this one transported me, with the aid of memory, to the early pages of *Oliver Twist*. We passed through cold-bleak passages, to which an odour of suet pudding, the aroma of Christmas cheer, failed to impart an air of hospitality; and then, after waiting a while in a little parlour appertaining to the superintendent, where the remainder of a dinner of by no means eleemosynary simplicity and the attitude of a gentleman asleep with a flushed face on the sofa seemed to effect a tacit exchange of references, we were ushered into a large frigid refectory, chiefly illumined by the twinkling tapers of the Christmas tree. Here entered to us some hundred and fifty little children of charity, who had been making a copious dinner and who brought with them an atmosphere of hunger memorably satisfied – together with other traces of the occasion upon their pinafores and their small red faces. I have said that the place reminded me of *Oliver Twist*, and I glanced through this little herd for an infant figure that should look as if it were cut out for romantic adventures. But they were all very prosaic little mortals. They were made of very common clay indeed, and a certain number of them were idiotic. They filed up and received their little offerings, and then they compressed themselves into a tight infantile bunch and, lifting up their small hoarse voices, directed a melancholy hymn toward their benefactress. The scene was a picture I shall not forget, with its curious mixture of poetry and sordid prose – the dying wintry light in the big bare, stale room; the beautiful Lady Bountiful, standing in the twinkling glory of the Christmas tree; the little multitude of staring and wondering, yet perfectly expressionless, faces.

Christmas Eve Ceremony

Robert Herrick

Come guard this night the Christmas-Pie,
That the thief, though ne'er so sly,
With his flesh-hooks, don't come nigh
To catch it

From him, who all alone sits there,
Having his eyes still in his ear,
And a deal of nightly fear
To watch it.

To Make Sack Posset

from *The Accomplisht Cook*, Robert May

Take two quarts of new cream, a quarter of an ounce of whole cinnamon, and two nutmegs quartered, boil it till it taste well of the spice, and keep it always stirring or it will burn too, then take the yolks of fourteen or fifteen eggs beaten well together with a little cold cream, put them to the cream on the fire, and stir it till it begin to boil, then take it off and sweeten it with sugar, and stir on till it be pretty cool; then take a pint and a quarter of sack, sweeten that also and set it on fire till it be ready to boil, then put it in a fine clean scoured bason, or posset pot, and pour the cream into it, elevating your hand to make it froth, which is the grace of your posset; if you put it through a tunnel or a cullender, it is held the more exquisite way.

The Christmas Tree at Windsor Castle

from the *Illustrated London News*

The Christmas Tree is annually prepared by her Majesty's command for the Royal children. Similar trees are arranged in other apartments of the Castle for her Majesty, his Royal Highness Prince Albert, her Royal Highness the Duchess of Kent, and the Royal household. The tree employed for this festive purpose if a young fir about eight feet high, and has six tiers of branches. On each tier, or branch, are arranged a dozen wax tapers. Pendent from the branches are elegant trays, baskets, *bonbonnières*, and other receptacles for sweetmeats, of the most varied and expensive kind; and of all forms, colours, and degrees of beauty. Fancy cakes, gilt gingerbread and eggs filled with sweetmeats, are also suspended by variously coloured ribbons from the branches. The tree, which stands upon a table covered with white damask, is supported at the root by piles of sweets of a larger kind, and by toys and dolls of all descriptions, suited to the youthful fancy, and to the several ages of the interesting scions of Royalty for whose gratification they are displayed. The name of each recipient is affixed to the doll, bonbon, or other present intended for it, so that no difference or opinion in the choice of dainties may arise to disturb the equanimity of the illustrious juveniles. On the summit of the tree stands the small figure of an angel, with outstretched wings, holding in each hand a wreath. Those trees are objects of much interest to all visitors at the Castle, from Christmas Eve, when they are first set up, until Twelfth Night, when they are finally removed. During this period two trees of similar magnitude and general design stand on the sideboard of the Royal Dining-room, and present a brilliant appearance when all the tapers are lighted up, among the branches. These trees are not accessible to the curiosity of the public; but her Majesty's visitors accompany the Queen from room to room to inspect them when they are illuminated. Her Majesty's tree is furnished by his Royal Highness Prince Albert, whilst that of the Prince is furnished according to the taste of her Majesty.

The Christmas Mummers' Play

Anon

The Christmas Mummers were folk plays performed by troupes of amateur actors known as mummers or guisers. They would be seen about towns, going from house to house, some of them wearing high conical caps of pasteboard decorated with ribbons and carrying wooden swords.

CAPTAIN SLASHER, *in military costume, with sword and pistol.*
KING OF ENGLAND, *in robes, wearing the crown.*
PRINCE GEORGE, *King's Son, in robes, and sword by his side.*
TURKISH CHAMPION, *in military attire, with sword and pistol.*
A NOBLE DOCTOR.
BEELZEBUB.
A CLOWN.

Enter Captain Slasher
I beg your pardon for being so bold,
I enter your house, the weather's so cold,

Room, a room! brave gallants, give us room to sport;
For in this house we do resort, –
Resort, resort, for many a day;
Step in, the King of England,
And boldly clear the way.

Enter the King of England
I am the King of England, that boldly does appear;
I come to seek my only son, – my only son is here.

Enter Prince George
I am Prince George, a worthy knight;
I'll spend my blood for England's right.
England's right I will maintain:
I'll fight for old England once again.

Enter Turkish Knight
I am the Turkish Champion:
From Turkey's land I come.
I come to fight the King of England
And all his noble men.

Captain Slasher
In comes Captain Slasher,
Captain Slasher is my name;
With sword and pistol by my side,
I hope to win the game.

King of England
I am the King of England,
As you may plainly see,
These are my soldiers standing by me;
They stand by me your life to end,
On them doth my life depend.

Prince George

I am Prince George, the Champion bold,
And with my sword I won three crowns of gold;
I slew the fiery dragon and brought him to the slaughter,
And won the King of Egypt's only daughter.

Turkish Champion

As I was going by St Francis' School,
I heard a lady cry 'A fool, a fool!'
'A fool', was every word,
'That man's a fool who wears a wooden sword.'

Prince George

A wooden sword, you dirty dog!
My sword is made of the best of metal free.
If you would like to taste of it,
I'll give it unto thee.
Stand off, stand off, you dirty dog!
Or by my sword you'll die.
I'll cut you down the middle,
And make your blood to fly.
[*They fight; Prince George falls, mortally wounded.*]

Enter King of England

Oh horrible! terrible! what hast thou done?
Thou hast ruin'd me, ruin'd me,
By killing of my only son!
Oh, is there ever a noble doctor to be found,
To cure this English champion
Of his deep and deadly wound?

Enter Noble Doctor

Oh yes, there is a noble doctor to be found,
To cure this English champion
Of his deep and deadly wound.

King of England

And pray what is your practice?

Noble Doctor

I boast not of my practice, neither do I study in the
practice of physic.

King of England

What can you cure?

Noble Doctor

All sorts of diseases,
Whatever you pleases:
I can cure the itch, the pitch,
The phthisic, the palsy and the gout;
And if the devil's in a man,
I can fetch him out.
My wisdom lies in my wig,
I torture not my patients with excations,
Such as pills, boluses, solutions, and embrocations;
But by the word of command
I can make this mighty Prince to stand.

King

What is your fee?

Doctor

Ten pounds is true.

King

Proceed, Noble Doctor;
You shall have your due.

Doctor

Arise, arise! most noble prince, arise,
And no more dormant lay;
And with thy sword
Make all thy foes obey.
[*The Prince arises.*]

Prince George

My head is made of iron,
My body is made of steel,
My legs are made of crooked bones
To force you all to yield.

Enter Beelzebub

In comes I, old Beelzebub,
Over my shoulder I carry my club,
And in my hand a frying-pan,
Pleased to get all the money I can.

Enter Clown

In come I, who's never been yet,
With my great head and little wit:
My head is great, my wit is small,
I'll do my best to please you all.

Song [*all join*]

And now we are done and must be gone,
No longer will we stay here;
But if you please, before we go,
We'll taste your Christmas beer.

Bertie's Christmas Eve

Saki

It was Christmas Eve, and the family circle of Luke Steffink, Esq., was aglow with the amiability and random mirth which the occasion demanded. A long and lavish dinner had been partaken of, waits had been round and sung carols; the house-party had regaled itself with more caroling on its own account, and there had been romping which, even in a pulpit reference, could not have been condemned as ragging. In the midst of the general glow, however, there was one black unkindled cinder.

Bertie Steffink, nephew of the aforementioned Luke, had early in life adopted the profession of ne'er-do-weel; his father had been something of the kind before him. At the age of eighteen Bertie had commenced that round of visits to our Colonial possessions, so seemly and desirable in the case of a Prince of the Blood, so suggestive of insincerity in a young man of the middle-class. He had gone to grow tea in Ceylon and fruit in British Columbia, and to help sheep to grow wool in Australia. At the age of twenty he had just returned from some similar errand in Canada, from which it may be gathered that the trial he gave to these various experiments was of the summary drumhead nature. Luke Steffink, who fulfilled the troubled role of guardian and deputy-parent to Bertie, deplored the persistent manifestation of the homing instinct on his nephew's part, and his solemn thanks earlier in the day for the blessing of reporting a united family had no reference to Bertie's return.

Arrangements had been promptly made for packing the youth off to a distant corner of Rhodesia, whence return would be a difficult matter; the journey to this uninviting destination was imminent, in fact a more careful and willing traveller would have already begun to think about his packing. Hence Bertie was in no mood to share in the festive spirit which displayed itself around him, and resentment smouldered within him at the eager, self-absorbed discussion of social plans for the coming months which he heard on all sides. Beyond depressing his uncle and the family circle generally by singing 'Say au revoir, and not goodbye', he had taken no part in the evening's conviviality.

Eleven o'clock had struck some half-hour ago, and the elder Steffinks began to throw out suggestions leading up to that process which they called retiring for the night.

'Come, Teddie, it's time you were in your little bed, you know,' said Luke Steffink to his thirteen-year-old son.

'That's where we all ought to be,' said Mrs Steffink.

'There wouldn't be room,' said Bertie.

The remark was considered to border on the scandalous; everybody ate raisins and almonds with the nervous industry of sheep feeding during threatening weather.

'In Russia,' said Horace Bordenby, who was staying in the house as a Christmas guest, 'I've read that the peasants believe that if you go into a cow-house or stable at midnight on Christmas Eve you will hear the animals talk. They're supposed to have the gift of speech at that one moment of the year.'

'Oh, DO let's ALL go down to the cow-house and listen to what they've got to say!' exclaimed Beryl, to whom anything was thrilling and amusing if you did it in a troop.

Mrs Steffink made a laughing protest, but gave a virtual consent by saying, 'We must all wrap up well, then.' The idea seemed a scatterbrained one to her, and almost heathenish, but it afforded an opportunity for 'throwing the young people together,' and as such she welcomed it. Mr Horace Bordenby was a young man with quite substantial prospects, and he had danced with Beryl at a local subscription ball a sufficient number of times to warrant the authorised inquiry on the part of the neighbours whether 'there was anything in it.' Though Mrs Steffink would not have put it in so many words, she shared the idea of the Russian peasantry that on this night the beast might speak.

The cow-house stood at the junction of the garden with a small paddock, an isolated survival, in a suburban neighbour-hood; of what had once been a small farm. Luke Steffink was complacently proud of his cow-house and his two cows; he felt that they gave him a stamp of solidity which no number of Wyandottes or Orpingtons could impart. They even seemed to link him in a sort of inconsequent way with those patriarchs who derived importance from their floating capital of flocks and herbs, he-asses and she-asses. It had been an anxious and momentous occasion when he had had to decide definitely between 'the Byre' and 'the Ranch' for the naming of his villa residence. A December midnight was hardly the moment he would have chosen for showing his farm-building to visitors, but since it was a fine night, and the young people were anxious for an excuse for a mild frolic, Luke consented to chaperon the expedition. The servants had long since gone to bed, so the house was left in charge of Bertie, who scornfully declined to stir out on the pretext of listening to bovine conversation.

'We must go quietly,' said Luke, as he headed the procession of giggling young folk, brought up in the rear by the shawled and hooded figure of Mrs Steffink; 'I've always laid stress on keeping this a quiet and orderly neighbourhood.'

It was a few minutes to midnight when the party reached the cow-house and made its way in by the light of Luke's stable lantern. For a moment every one stood in silence, almost with a feeling of being in church.

'Daisy – the one lying down – is by a shorthorn bull out of a Guernsey cow,' announced Luke in a hushed voice, which was in keeping with the foregoing impression.

'Is she?' said Bordenby, rather as if he had expected her to be by Rembrandt.

'Myrtle is—'

Myrtle's family history was cut short by a little scream from the women of the party.

The cow-house door had closed noiselessly behind them and the key had turned gratingly in the lock; then they heard Bertie's voice pleasantly wishing them good night and his footsteps retreating along the garden path.

Luke Steffink strode to the window; it was a small square opening of the old-fashioned sort, with iron bars let into the stonework.

'Unlock the door this instant,' he shouted, with as much air of menacing authority as a hen might assume when screaming through the bars of a coop at a marauding hawk. In reply to his summons the hall door closed with a defiant bang.

A neighbouring clock struck the hour of midnight. If the cows had received the gift of human speech at that moment they would not have been able to make themselves heard. Seven or eight other voices were engaged in describing Bertie's present conduct and his general character at a high pressure of excitement and indignation.

In the course of half an hour or so everything that it was permissible to say about Bertie had been said some dozens of times, and other topics began to come to the front – the extreme mustiness of the cow-house, the possibility of it catching fire, and the probability of it being a Rowton House for the vagrant rats of the neighbourhood. And still no sign of deliverance came to the unwilling vigil-keepers.

Towards one o'clock the sound of rather boisterous and undisciplined carol singing approached rapidly, and came to a sudden anchorage, apparently just outside the garden gate. A motorload of youthful 'bloods', in a high state of conviviality, had made a temporary halt for repairs; the stoppage, however, did not extend to the vocal efforts of the party, and the watchers in the cowshed were treated to a highly unauthorised rendering of 'Good King Wenceslas', in which the adjective 'good' appeared to be very carelessly applied.

The noise had the effect of bringing Bertie out into the garden, but he utterly ignored the pale, angry faces peering out at the cow-house window, and concentrated his attention on the revellers outside the gate.

'Wassail, you chaps!' he shouted.

'Wassail, old sport!' they shouted back; 'we'd jolly well drink y'r health, only we've nothing to drink it in.'

'Come and wassail inside,' said Bertie hospitably; 'I'm all alone, and there's heaps of "wet".'

They were total strangers, but his touch of kindness made them instantly his kin. In another moment the unauthorised version of King Wenceslas, which, like many other scandals, grew worse on repetition, went echoing up the garden path; two of the revellers gave an impromptu performance on the way by executing the staircase waltz up the terraces of what Luke Steffink, hitherto with some justification, called his rock-garden. The rock part of it was still there when the waltz had been accorded its third encore. Luke, more than ever like a cooped hen behind the cow-house bars, was in a position to realise the feelings of concert goers unable to countermand the call for an encore which they neither desire or deserve.

The hall door closed with a bang on Bertie's guests, and the sounds of merriment became faint and muffled to the weary watchers at the other end of the garden. Presently two ominous pops, in quick succession, made themselves distinctly heard.

'They've got at the champagne!' exclaimed Mrs Steffink.

'Perhaps it's the sparkling Moselle,' said Luke hopefully.

Three or four more pops were heard.

'The champagne and the sparkling Moselle,' said Mrs Steffink.

Luke uncorked an expletive which, like brandy in a temperance household, was only used on rare emergencies. Mr Horace Bordenby had been making use of similar expressions under his breath for a considerable time past. The experiment of 'throwing the young people together' had been prolonged beyond a point when it was likely to produce any romantic result.

Some forty minutes later the hall door opened and disgorged a crowd that had thrown off any restraint of shyness that might have influenced its earlier actions. Its vocal efforts in the direction of carol singing were now supplemented by instrumental music; a Christmas tree that had been prepared for the children of the gardener and other household retainers had yielded a rich spoil of tin trumpets, rattles, and drums. The life-story of King Wenceslas had been dropped, Luke was thankful to notice, but it was intensely irritating for the chilled prisoners in the cow-house to be told that it was a hot time in the old town tonight, together with some accurate but entirely superfluous information as to the imminence of Christmas morning. Judging by the protests which began to be shouted from the upper windows of neighbouring houses the sentiments prevailing in the cow-house were heartily echoed in other quarters.

The revellers found their car, and, what was more remarkable, managed to drive off in it, with a parting fanfare of tin trumpets. The lively beat of a drum disclosed the fact that the master of the revels remained on the scene.

'Bertie!' came in an angry, imploring chorus of shouts and screams from the cow-house window.

'Hullo,' cried the owner of the name, turning his rather errant steps in the direction of the summons; 'are you people still there? Must have heard everything cows got to say by this time. If you haven't, no use waiting. After all, it's a Russian legend, and Russian Chrismush Eve not due for 'other fortnight. Better come out.'

After one or two ineffectual attempts he managed to pitch the key of the cow-house door in through the window. Then, lifting his voice in the strains of 'I'm afraid to go home in the dark', with a lusty drum accompaniment, he led the way back to the house. The hurried procession of the released that followed in his steps came in for a good deal of the adverse comment that his exuberant display had evoked.

It was the happiest Christmas Eve he had ever spent. To quote his own words, he had a rotten Christmas.

The Christmas Tree

C. Day Lewis

Put out the lights now!
Look at the Tree, the rough tree dazzled
In oriole plumes of flame,
Tinselled with twinkling frost fire, tasselled
With stars and moons – the same
That yesterday hid in the spinney and had no fame
Till we put out the lights now.

Hard are the nights now:
The fields at moonrise turn to agate,
Shadows are cold as jet;
In dyke and furrow, in copse and faggot
The frost's tooth is set;
And stars are the sparks whirled out by the north wind's
    fret
On the flinty nights now.

So feast your eyes now
On mimic star and moon-cold bauble;

79

Worlds may wither unseen,
But the Christmas Tree is a tree of fable,
A phoenix in evergreen,
And the world cannot change or chill what its mysteries
    mean
To your hearts and eyes now.

The vision dies now
Candle by candle: the tree that embraced it
Returns to its own kind,
To be earthed again and weather as best it
May the frost and the wind.
Children, it too had its hour – you will not mind
If it lives or dies now.

Christmas Eve, 1667

Samuel Pepys

Up, and all the morning at the office, and at noon with my
clerks to dinner, and then to the office again, busy at the office
till six at night, and then by coach to St James's, it being
about six at night; my design being to see the ceremonys, this
night being the eve of Christmas, at the Queen's chapel. But
it being not begun I to Westminster Hall, and there staid and
walked, and then to the Swan, and there drank and talked, and
did banter a little Frank, and so to White Hall, and sent my
coach round, I through the Park to chapel, where I got in up
almost to the rail, and with a great deal of patience staid from
nine at night to two in the morning, in a very great crowd;
and there expected, but found nothing extraordinary, there

being nothing but a high masse. The Queen was there, and some ladies. But, Lord! what an odde thing it was for me to be in a crowd of people, here a footman, there a beggar, here a fine lady, there a zealous poor papist, and here a Protestant, two or three together, come to see the shew. I was afeard of my pocket being picked very much . . . Their musique very good indeed, but their service I confess too frivolous, that there can be no zeal go along with it, and I do find by them themselves that they do run over their beads with one hand, and point and play and talk and make signs with the other in the midst of their masse. But all things very rich and beautiful; and I see the papists have the wit, most of them, to bring cushions to kneel on, which I wanted, and was mightily troubled to kneel. All being done . . . I left people receiving the Sacrament: and the Queen gone, and ladies; only my Lady Castlemayne, who looked prettily in her night-clothes, and so took my coach, which waited, and away through Covent Garden, to set down two gentlemen and a lady, who come thither to see also, and did make mighty mirth in their talk of the folly of this religion. And so I stopped, having set them down and drank some burnt wine at the Rose Tavern door, while the constables come, and two or three Bellmen went by, it being a fine, light, moonshine morning, and so home round the city, and stopped and dropped money at five or six places, which I was the willinger to do, it being Christmas-day, and so home, and there find my wife in bed, and Jane and the maids making pyes, and so I to bed, and slept well, and rose about nine, and to church, and there heard a dull sermon of Mr Mills, but a great many fine people at church; and so home. Wife and girl and I alone at dinner – a good Christmas dinner, and all the afternoon at home, my wife reading to me 'The History of the Drummer of Mr Mompesson', which is a strange story of spies, and worth reading indeed. In the evening comes Mr Pelling, and he sat and supped with us; and very good company, he reciting to us many copies of good verses of Dr Wilde, who writ 'Iter Boreale', and so to bed.

Letter home from Italy, 1919

Lieutenant-Colonel Robert Joyce Clarke

Lieutenant-Colonel Robert Joyce Clarke was a territorial officer in the Royal Berkshire Regiment. He wrote this letter to his wife on 12 January 1919 from Italy.

Very little has happened the last week, only two matters of interest. Firstly the rains never stopped for five days & six nights, & the rivers were all raging torrents. They were a sight, whole trees were rooted up & swept down, light bridges were washed away, & the local people were very anxious, no one had ever seen the like. I understood why the river banks are built so high & so strongly, of course the rush of water from the mountains is enormous. The current was over twelve miles an hour. The course of the river changed its side, before the flood it was on the left, after it was on the right side. I had heard before that this often happens, still it was interesting to see it. Secondly our children's party on the 6th was a great success. They all assembled in the village schoolrooms, it was to begin at 5.30 but at 4 they began to arrive! We expected about 120, when I went into the two rooms I counted over 90 in each, & a few more came in later. The Xmas tree was lighted up & we, that is the Officers & Sergeants, made a procession from the schools to the old aura (this is our Canteen and concert hall etc) it holds about 350 sitting on forms etc. Each of us took a small girl, & all the rest of the kids followed on. We walked round the tree & waited, about half the Sergeants were in fancy dress, any kind of dress too! Then the Adjutant & Green, one of the Subalterns, came in dressed as Father Xmas & his wife. Here Father Xmas is not the bringer of toys etc but an old woman called 'Bifana', so our idea worked well. The Adjutant made a short speech in Italian, & then began to give away the presents from the tree. We had bought 150 presents & there were about 100 decorations on the tree too. The place was packed, for odd parents had pushed their way in too. The noise was deafening for we had a made-up band of tin trumpets, bugles, drums, any odd thing etc & they never ceased. The kids crowded round & I hope everyone got something. Then we took the tree away, & gave them cocoa, biscuits, sandwiches of bread & bully beef, cheese & jam, over 1,000 were eaten. Then we gave an enter-tainment of sorts, & a dancing bear, elephant, horse, dancers etc all came in & performed – the kids were a bit frightened at first, but they soon got used to them. As they went away, we gave them each two oranges & a card. They all really enjoyed themselves & I get smiles from each kid when I meet them now! The village schoolmistress is a wonderful organiser, I am sure – she has all the kids so well behaved. She sent me such a pretty little view of Venice, I think it is, in oil asking if she might be Bifana to me, a pretty idea. Tell Mother I sent her 15 photos by one of my subalterns going on leave today, they ought to arrive about the 19th. Can't think of any more news.

The Curate's Christmas Eve

Harold Monro

The Curate and the Spinster sit.
(O gentle dear timidity!)
Her yearning thought, his untried wit,
Her aspidistra and their tea
Combine to make their Christmas Eve complete
Within itself; and neither sour nor sweet.

Why should the moralist complain?
The sentimentalist deride?
She turns fond eyes on him in vain:
She will not ever be a bride,
For he is doomed to pass eternity
Sipping, O, nothing more than, sipping tea.

She will not be compelled to scold,
Nor he driven to complain.
They are both better than any gold.
No mistletoe, and no champagne,
Will make her less a main, him more a priest,
Or turn their Christian to a pagan feast.

Harking Back Long Ago

Winifred Holtby

In the dark nursery at the back of the long grey brick farm-house, my sister and I lay awake on Christmas Eve. I was four and she was six-and-a-half, and the hour seemed to us prodigiously, daringly, joyously late. It was a quarter to ten on a bright frosty night, and through the square, uncurtained window the stars glistened, mapped out into unastronomical constellations by the woodwork between the small square panes, just as on our nursery map the continents were marked off into squares by the lines of latitude and longitude. The maids who had been clattering in the pantry below us were silent; in the horse-pasture beyond the garden an iron-shod hoof once clanked heavily on the frozen field road; the night was very still. We lay – not speaking – listening.

Then it came. We sat up in bed, all ears, and heard it; the crunch of feet on the gravel of the drive, the shuffling as men took their places round the light of a single lantern, the schoolmaster's muffled. 'One – two – three' –

> *Hark, the herald angels sing*
> *Glory to the new-born King.*

We were out of bed. We were scampering barefoot along the nursery passage, up two steps into the bad bit of unlighted corridor, past the silver cupboard that harboured ghosts and tigers, on to the front landing and through a door into the best spare room. And peering between the slits of the Venetian blind, there we saw them. The grown-ups had not gone to bed; they had drawn back the curtains from the drawing-room windows, and the lamplight streamed out on to the gravel drive. In moonlight, and starlight, and lamplight, and lantern-light stood the singers. Their faces were pale and their long coats black dark, but here and there a scarlet muffler or a pair of fine, glowing cheeks caught the lamplight. There were twenty men and boys from the choir standing round the schoolmaster's lantern, singing:

> *Peace on earth and mercy mi-ild*
> *God and sinners reconciled.*

The draught blew in through the cold bedroom; the chill air was sharp as eau de Cologne, as icy water, on our bodies; we gathered our night-dresses around us and huddled together for warmth.

> *Mild he lays His glory by*
> *Born that man no more may die.*

I can close my eyes and see them; I can shut my ears and hear them; in the warmth of my lighted room I can feel the wind on my bare arms, and the chill boards under my naked feet. I can even smell the queer cold, smoky, frosty smell of the unused bedroom. It is all there.

But it is mine. Nobody else can ever hear it as I heard and hear it. No other living memory now carries the echo of those particular singers in that particular garden, though a million children have stolen from bed and scampered like mice through a dark house to hear the carollers on Christmas Eve. When I die, nobody will ever again know that particular sweet fierce exaltation which stirred the rapturous, unblurred magination of a child.

Or will they? Suppose it comes true. Suppose that men do one day invent a machine which will listen to the past, pick up the sound waves as they slide off the air waves on to the ether, and reproduce for us all sounds that have ever been. Then, perhaps, turning a dial carelessly, a dry-goods salesman in Chicago, or a herdsman in Kenya, or a silk merchant in Rangoon, may suddenly hear the crunch of feet on gravel outside a Yorkshire farmhouse, and the schoolmaster's breathy 'One, two, three,' and the burst of singing that summoned two children from their beds.

But I do not think that that particular little private ecstasy will be recaptured. The world has heard too many Christmas sounds of more imposing significance. If I had my own way, my instrument that listened to the past, my table of dates and latitudes and longitudes, and if I could eavesdrop when and where I would among the centuries, what Christmas Festival would I summon? My own Christmases live in my own memory. I do not need the delicate, terrifying omniscience of an instrument to tune in for me on to the sound of WAACS and English Tommies in a hut under French orchard trees toasting the First Christmas after the Armistice in claret cup. I need no help to hear again the village choir, with the squire's son playing the cornet, braying out into 'O come, all ye faithful', at the vestry door, nor to hear the sound of crackers exploding round the table, nor the gasping scurry at the front door as small children broke in upon us with 'I-wish-you-merry-Christmas-n'a'ppy-New-Year-'n-please-will-yer-give's-a-Christmas-box?' nor to hear the shouting of the maids and their young men and my nieces and the rest of us dancing round the Christmas tree, blowing out candles to the tune of:

> *Sally went round the sun,*
> *Sally went round the moon,*
> *Sally went round the chimney pots*
> *On a Christmas afternoon. Pouff!*
> *Sally went round the sun.*

And so on, till the last candle was extinguished with a triumphant 'Pouff!'

All that is done. All that is mine. But there are others whose Christmas memories I would most joyously purloin. I think I would turn my dial to Rome, and to the year AD 800, the year before Pope Leo III had been maltreated in the streets, and had appealed for protection to the Frankish king, the great Charles, Charlemagne, the conqueror of Pavia, the conqueror of the Saxons, the patron of the Church, the Hammer of Christendom. Big and robust in frame he was, measuring about seven of his feet in height, great hunter, and ruler, and father; like Solomon, the lover of many concubines, like Judah, a brave begetter of sons. The Church was beset by enemies; the Lombards in the north of Italy, the pagans in Germany, the heathen round the Mediterranean. The Empire had shifted its headquarters to Byzantium. The Pope was left, guardian not only of the spirit but of the body of Christendom, and times were hard. In the year 800, Charlemagne marched to Rome 'to restore order', and on Christmas Day he knelt in the church of Saint Peter, the most powerful worshipper in the Western world. And behold, as he rose up from prayer, the Pope set on his head the imperial crown, and proclaimed him Holy Roman Emperor in the name of the Father and of the Son and of the Holy Ghost, and all the people applauded and the warriors in the streets outside clashed their weapons, and it was as though the voice of the people spoke with the voice of God, hailing the birth of a new epoch. It was the birth of a new epoch. From that cry arose the Holy Roman Empire, and the Middle Ages, and Dante's dream of a unified Christendom. And I envy the New Zealanders and Latvians and Brazilians of the future who will one day tune in to hear that epoch-making tumult.

But while my hand was on the dial I would turn back. The Venerable Bede once told us 'that the ancient people of the Angli began the year on the 25th of December, when we now celebrate the birthday of Our Lord; and the very night which is now so holy to us, they called in their tongue "modranecht" (modra niht) – that is, the mother's night – by reason, we suspect, of the ceremonies which in that night-long vigil they performed.' I should not understand a word of the rough tongue spoken by my forefathers in their pagan Christmas; I should only hear shouts and the rattle of oaken spears, perhaps, and the grinding of stones, and perhaps the shriek of a victim sacrificed. Or would there be a gentler ritual on modranecht, mother's night? I should like to hear.

I should like to listen to the first English Christmas after Charles II, the Merry Monarch, came back to his kingdom, and banished the gloom of the Puritan festival with laughter, and feasts, and dancing. I should like to tune in to the court of Saint James, where the jokes might be a trifle coarse, and where the noblest princes would belch and spit like coal heavers; but my loud-speaker would only give me sound, not scent nor sight. The flickering candlelight, the heat from the great fires, the stew of sweat and paint, and stuffiness and cooking, and perfume and humanity, and wine and cosmetics would be lost to me. But I might hear the King's deep, witty voice, and Lady Castlemaine's mad, musical laughter. There are conveniences about a medium which appeals to one sense only.

And while I was in London, and Westminster, and the seventeenth century, should I tune in to the year 1662, and go with Mr Pepys to the chapel in Whitehall, coming 'too late to receive communion with the family', but in time enough to hear Bishop Morley preach upon the song of the Angels, 'Glory to God on high, on earth peace, and good will towards men'? No. Here I think eyes are better than ears, for I would rather read Pepys' ever-unspoken comment, 'A poor sermon, but long'. How excellent that 'but', as though length compensated for poverty in preaching! I would rather listen on another year to the Pepys household. '1668. Christmas Day. – To dine alone with my wife, who, poor wretch! sat undressed all day till ten at night, altering and lacing of a noble petticoat; while I by her making the boy read to me the *Life of Julius Caesar* and *Des Cartes' Book of Musick*.' I should hear the boy's voice, and the rustle of Mrs Pepys' noble silk and her husband's yawn as he turned from Julius Caesar.

Slowly, slowly the dial would turn, and the years fall away, and I think that one place I would linger would be on no land, but 'in the chops of the Channel, with the Scilly Isles on a vague bearing within thirty miles of us, and not a breath of wind anywhere'. And there I should find the young Korzeniowski, encountering his captain on a foggy morning, with the ship 'wrapped up in a damp blanket and as motionless as a post', and I should hear the Polish sailor politely greet his superior in English with 'Merry Christmas, sir,' and the grimly-scathing reply, 'Looks like it, doesn't it?' Or is it better to restrain the dial and read instead the account of it all in Joseph Conrad's own essay, *Christmas Day at Sea*?

The world would then be mine, and all the sounds thereof. I might swing round the globe to New Zealand, to listen to a picnic party in the sweltering sun, eating plum pudding in the bush – a grim achievement which yet might sound the same as any Christmas dinner in an English country house, with snow and mistletoe and robins. I might go south to a lonely hut in the vast wilderness of the Antarctic, and listen to a small company of gentlemen making merry with their leader, one Captain Scott. Or, while I was visiting adventures, I might find the year of grace 1497; the place, a green-wooded bay dipping down to the Indian Ocean; the scene, a wooden ship sailing through mild summer weather; the day, Christmas Day, and the excited cries – unhappily for me, in Portuguese – as Terra Natalis, the land of Christmas, Natal first was named. Anything less like a Christmas land than that fair province, half upland, half semi-tropical coast, I hardly can imagine. But there would be a sound of water, and the bells of the ship, and the rattle of ropes, and the noise of wind in the sails, and the voices of the sailors. I could hear well enough to distinguish the boat, poor linguist though I am, if I listened. And, using my privilege, I might steal inland, and hear other cries, the amazement of black watchers on the shore as, in the words of an old carol, they 'saw a ship come sailing by, on Christmas Day in the morning'.

I could have tropical Christmases and Arctic Christmases, Christmases pagan and Christian, ancient and modern, a grim Christmas with John Knox, a lofty Christmas with Sir Walter Raleigh on the high seas, a jovial Christmas with a bourgeois German family in the last century. And I know that some will ask me, and I should ask myself, why, since I have the power, should I not go back two thousand years, to Palestine, to a village inn, and an inn stable? For there, though I could not understand the language, and though the noises from the streets would all be strange to me, I might hear the cattle moving in their stalls as I have heard them in the dark shed near our farmhouse; I might hear voices, and a hurrying to and from the crowded inn, and the questioning of shepherds, and the cry of a child.

I might. But then, I might not. Sounds are confusing. One night is strangely like another night. I have heard a small child crying, and his mother's voice comforting him. I have heard the humble, homely rustlings, and munchings, and stirrings of cattle among the straw; I have heard shepherds striding down from the hills to a village inn. And among so many sounds, how should we know the sound that changed a world? What was one mother's voice among the village women? Or one child's cry in that crowded town?

The shout of the Frankish warriors when Charles the Great was crowned, the thundering of Bishop Morley rating the Court, the laugh of Lady Castlemaine – these would be easier to distinguish than those quiet sounds.

> *He cam al so stylle*
> *Where his moder was*
> *As dewe in Aprylle*
> *That fallyt on the gras.*

> *He cam al so stylle*
> *To his moder's bowr*
> *As dewe in Aprylle*
> *That fallyt on the flour.*

I would rather turn to a much later Christmas and hear in a Kent village a girl's voice singing that ballad. Its fresh sweetness tells us more than we might learn from our most ingenious instrument, our most erudite expert in Semitic languages.

I am glad that we have more than one sense through which to perceive the world. I am glad that when all the five senses are stilled memory takes up the tale. I am content to leave some sounds to memory and imagination.

The Stock Exchange Carol

J. B. Morton

Swift we be come on joyful feet,
Through wind and snow from Lombard Street,
To tell glad tidings far and wide
Of Patagonian Allied.

Noel, Noel, Noel, Noel!
Sing jolly men, who buy and sell,
For Trans. Rhd. Corp. (ex bonus) Tea
Has risen again to 93.

Lo! Far and near we hear the call,
And Belgian Zinc's begun to fall,
Sing we and tell with joyous tongue
How badly old Sir George was stung.
Noel, Noel, etc.

Bright is the light, and wild, and strange,
That shines above the Stock Exchange;
Contentment crowns the happy scene –
There is a boom in Margarine.
Noel, Noel, etc.

High over all a Voice is heard –
'Lord Funck is buying Tin Preferred!'
Loud chaunts th'angelic syndicate,
'Sell out, sell out at 48!'
Noel, Noel, etc.

A Reproof for King Arthur

from *History of York*, 1785

AT this time (A.D. 521) that great Monarch Arthur, with his Clergy, all his Nobility, and Soldiers, kept *Christmas* in *York*, whither resorted to him the prime Persons of the Neighbourhood, and spent the latter End of *December* in Mirth, Jollity, Drinking and the Vices that are too often the Consequence of them; so that the Representations of the old Heathenish Feasts dedicated to Saturn were here again revived; but the Number of Days they lasted were doubled and amongst the wealthier Sort trebled; during which Time they counted it almost a Sin to treat of any serious Matter. Gifts are sent mutually from and to one another; frequent invitations pass betwixt Friends, and domestick Offenders are not punished. Our Countrymen call this Jule-tide, substituting the name of *Julius Cæsar* for that of *Saturn*. The Vulgar are yet persuaded that the Nativity of Christ is then celebrated, but mistakenly; for 'tis plain they imitate the Lasciviousness of *Bacchanalians*, rather than the memory of *Christ*, then, as they say, born.

The Ghost

from *Hamlet*, William Shakespeare

BARNARDO: 'Tis here!
HORATIO: 'Tis here!
MARCELLUS: 'Tis gone!
[Exit GHOST.]
MARCELLUS: It faded on the crowing of the cock.
    Some say that ever 'gainst that season comes
    Wherein our Saviour's birth is celebrated,
    The bird of dawning singeth all night long:
    And then, they say, no spirit dares stir abroad;
    The nights are wholesome; then no planets strike,
    No fairy takes, nor witch hath power to charm,
    So hallow'd and so gracious is the time.
HORATIO: So have I heard, and do in part believe it.

A Land Girl's Diary, 1939

Gwenda Morgan

Gwenda Morgan was a painter and wood-engraver from Petworth, Sussex. When the Women's Land Army was formed in June 1939, Gwenda Morgan was in one of the first two groups of 'Land Girls' trained prior to the outbreak of war.

Dec 24 Poultry. Dung spreading. Miserable day, dull. Asked about Christmas holiday, Mr W. said Boxing Day wasn't considered to be holiday for men but I could have it if I liked, so I said

I would like and thanked him very much. I didn't really think the men *would* have to work on Boxing Day, but at 5 o'c I saw pigman and he said, yes, and that Mr W. hadn't told them they must until the middle of the afternoon. No Christmas feeling on the farm at all. Wretched. I felt quite miserable in spite of the prospect of two days' holiday. Felt alright when I got home, though. Went up to Helen and May Austin with present (chocs) and then decorated house with holly. Hope the war will be over this time next year. O! how I hope. Package of my pictures arrived from Green & Stone (one cut by flying glass in a raid). If only I had the chance of painting now, I could do something much better than these, I am sure.

Christmas Invitation

William Barnes

Come done to-morrow night; an' mind,
Don't leave thy fiddle-bag behind;
We'll sheake a lag an' drink a cup
O'eale, to keep wold Chris'mas up.

You won't meet any stranger's feace,
But only naighbours o' the pleace,
An' Stowe, an' Combe; an' two or dree
Vrom uncle's up at Rookery.

An' thou wu'lt vind a rwosy feace,
An' peair ov eyes so black as sloos,
The prettiest woones in all the pleace,—
I'm sure I needen tell thee whose.

We got a back-bran', dree gre't logs
So much as dree ov us can car;
We'll put em up athirt the dogs,
An' meake a vier to the bar.

An' ev'ry woone shall tell his teale,
An' ev'ry woone shall zing his zong,
An' ev'ry woone wull drink his eale,
To love an' friend'ship all night long.

We'll snap the tongs, we'll have a ball,
We'll sheake the house, we'll life the ruf,
We'll romp an' meake the maidens squall,
A catchen o'm at blind-man's buff.

Going a Hodening

from *The Mirror of Literature, Amusement and Instruction,* 1832

At Ramsgate they commence their Christmas festivities by
the following ceremony: A party of the youthful portion of
the community having procured the head of a horse, it is
affixed to a pole, about four feet in length; a string is attached
to the lower jaw, a horse cloth is tied round the extreme part
of the head, beneath which one of the party is concealed,
who, by repeated pulling and loosening the string, causes the
jaw to rise and fall, and thus produces, by bringing the teeth
in contact, a snapping noise, as he moves along; the rest of the
party following in procession, grotesquely habited, and ringing hand-bells. In this order they proceed from house to
house, singing carols and ringing their bells, and are generally

remunerated for the amusement they occasion by a largess of money, or beer and cake. This ceremony is called 'a hoodening'. The figure which we have described is designated 'a hooden' or wooden horse. The ceremony prevails in many parts of the Isle of Thanet, and may probably be traces as the relic of some religious ceremony practised in the early ages by our Saxon ancestors.

Humbug

from *A Christmas Carol*, Charles Dickens

Once upon a time – of all the good days in the year, on Christmas Eve – old Scrooge sat busy in his counting-house. It was cold, bleak, biting weather: foggy withal: and he could hear the people in the court outside, go wheezing up and down, beating their hands upon their breasts, and stamping their feet upon the pavement stones to warm them. The city clocks had only just gone three, but it was quite dark already: it had not been light all day: and candles were flaring in the windows of the neighbouring offices, like ruddy smears upon the palpable brown air. The fog came pouring in at every chink and keyhole, and was so dense without, that although the court was of the narrowest, the houses opposite were mere phantoms. To see the dingy cloud come drooping down, obscuring everything, one might have thought that Nature lived hard by, and was brewing on a large scale.

The door of Scrooge's counting-house was open that he might keep his eye upon his clerk, who in a dismal little cell beyond, a sort of tank, was copying letters. Scrooge had a very small fire, but the clerk's fire was so very much smaller that it looked like one coal. But he couldn't replenish it, for Scrooge kept the coal-box in his own room; and so surely as the clerk came in with the shovel, the master predicted that it would be necessary for them to part. Wherefore the clerk put on his white comforter, and tried to warm himself at the candle; in which effort, not being a man of a strong imagination, he failed.

'A merry Christmas, uncle! God save you!' cried a cheerful voice. It was the voice of Scrooge's nephew, who came upon him so quickly that this was the first intimation he had of his approach.

'Bah!' said Scrooge, 'Humbug!'

He had so heated himself with rapid walking in the fog and frost, this nephew of Scrooge's, that he was all in a glow; his face was ruddy and handsome; his eyes sparkled, and his breath smoked again.

'Christmas a humbug, uncle!' said Scrooge's nephew. 'You don't mean that, I am sure.'

'I do,' said Scrooge. 'Merry Christmas! What right have you to be merry? What reason have you to be merry? You're poor enough.'

'Come, then,' returned the nephew gaily. 'What right have you to be dismal? What reason have you to be morose? You're rich enough.'

Scrooge having no better answer ready on the spur of the moment, said, 'Bah!' again; and followed it up with 'Humbug.'

'Don't be cross, uncle,' said the nephew.

'What else can I be,' returned the uncle, 'when I live in such a world of fools as this Merry Christmas! Out upon merry Christmas. What's Christmas time to you but a time for paying bills without money; a time for finding yourself a year older, but not an hour richer; a time for balancing your books and having every item in 'em through a round dozen of months presented dead against you? If I could work my will,' said Scrooge indignantly, 'every idiot who goes about with "Merry Christmas" on his lips, should be boiled with his own pudding, and buried with a stake of holly through his heart. He should!'

'Uncle!' pleaded the nephew.

'Nephew!' returned the uncle, sternly, 'keep Christmas in your own way, and let me keep it in mine.'

The Carol of the Poor Children

Richard Middleton

We are the poor children, come out to see the sights
On this day of all days, on this night of nights;
The stars in merry parties are dancing in the sky,
A fine star, a new star, is shining on high!

We are the poor children, our lips are frosty blue,
We cannot sing our carol as well as rich folk do;
Our bellies are so empty we have no singing voice,
But this night of all nights good children must rejoice.

We do rejoice, we do rejoice, as hard as we can try,
A fine star, a new star is shining in the sky!
And while we sing our carol, we think of the delight
The happy kings and shepherds make in Bethlehem
    to-night.

Are we naked, mother, and are we starving-poor –
Oh, see what gifts the kings have brought outside the
    stable door;
Are we cold, mother, the ass will give his hay
To make the manger warm and keep the cruel winds away.

We are the poor children, but not so poor who sing
Our carol with our voiceless hearts to greet the new-
  born King,
On this night of all nights, when in the frosty sky
A new star, a kind star is shining on high!

The Father Christmas letter, *1941*

J. R. R. Tolkien

Between 1920 and 1943, J. R. R. Tolkien wrote a series of letters for his children, from Father Christmas and his elf secretary. They documented the adventures and misadventures of Father Christmas and his helpers, including the North Polar Bear and his two mischievous cubs, Paksu and Valkotukka.

I am so glad you did not forget to write to me again this year. The number of children who keep up with me seems to be getting smaller. I expect it is because of this horrible war, and that when it is over things will improve again, and I shall be as busy as ever. But at present so terribly many people have lost their homes, or have left them; half the world seems in the wrong place! And even up here we have been having troubles. I don't mean only with my stores; of course they are getting low. They were already low last year, and I have not been able to fill them up, so that I have to send what I can, instead of what is asked for. But worse than that has happened.

I expect you remember that some years ago we had trouble with the Goblins, and we thought we had settled it. Well, it broke out again this autumn, worse than it has been for centuries. We have had several battles, and for a while my house was besieged. In November it began to look likely that it would be captured, and all my goods, and that Christmas stockings would remain empty all over the world. Would not that have been a calamity?

It has not happened – and that is largely due to the efforts of Polar Bear – but it was not until the beginning of this month that I was able to send out any messengers! I expect the Goblins thought that with so much war going on, this was a fine chance to recapture the North. They must have been preparing for some years; and they made a huge new tunnel which had an outlet many miles away. It was early in October that they suddenly came out in thousands. Polar Bear says there were at least a million, but that is his favourite big number. Anyway, he was still fast asleep at the time, and I was rather drowsy myself; the weather was rather warm for the time of the year, and Christmas seemed far away. There were only one or two elves about the place; and of course Paksu and Valkotukka (also fast asleep). The Penguins had all gone away in the spring. Luckily Goblins cannot help yelling and beating on drums when they mean to fight; so we all woke up in time, and got the gates and doors barred and the windows shuttered. Polar Bear got on the roof and fired rockets into the Goblin hosts as they poured up the long reindeer-drive; but that did not stop them for long. We were soon surrounded.

I have not time to tell you all the story. I had to blow three blasts on the great Horn (Windbeam). It hangs over the fire-place in the hall, and if I have not told you about it before, it is because I have not had to blow it for over four hundred years. Its sound carries as far as the North Wind blows. All the same, it was three whole days before help came: snow-boys, Polar Bears, and hundreds and hundreds of elves. They came up behind the Goblins; and Polar Bear (really awake this time) rushed out with a blazing branch off the fire in each paw. He must have killed dozens of Goblins (he says a million).

But there was a big battle down in the plain near the North Pole in November, in which the Goblins brought hundreds of new companies out of their tunnels. We were driven back to the Cliff, and it was not until Polar Bear and a party of his younger relatives crept out by night, and blew up the entrance to the new tunnels with nearly 100 lbs of gun-powder, that we got the better of them – for the present. But bang went all the stuff for making fireworks and crackers (the cracking part) for some years. The North Pole cracked and fell over (for the second time) and we have not yet had time to mend it. Polar Bear is rather a hero (I hope he does not think so himself). But of course he is a very *magical* animal really, and Goblins can't do much to him when he is awake and angry. I have seen their arrows bouncing off him and breaking.

Well, that will give you some idea of events, and you will understand why I have not had time to draw a picture this year – rather a pity, because there have been such exciting things to draw – and why I have not been able to collect the usual things for you, or even the very few that you asked for . . .

FATHER CHRISTMAS

The Oxen

Thomas Hardy

Christmas Eve, and twelve of the clock.
'Now they are all on their knees,'
An elder said as we sat in a flock
By the embers in hearthside ease.

We pictured the meek mild creatures where
They dwelt in their strawy pen,
Nor did it occur to one of us there
To doubt they were kneeling then.

So fair a fancy few would weave
In these years! Yet, I feel,
If someone said on Christmas Eve,
'Come; see the oxen kneel,

'In the lonely barton by yonder coomb
Our childhood used to know,'
I should go with him in the gloom,
Hoping it might be so.

CHRISTMAS DAY

On the Morning of Christ's Nativity

John Milton

This is the month, and this the happy morn,
Wherein the Son of Heaven's eternal King,
Of wedded maid and Virgin Mother born,
Our great redemption from above did bring;
For so the holy sages once did sing,
That he our deadly forfeit should release,
And with his Father work us a perpetual peace [. . .]

Say, Heavenly Muse, shall not thy sacred vein
Afford a present to the Infant God?
Hast thou no verse, no hymn, or solemn strain,
To welcome him to this his new abode,
Now while the heaven, by the Sun's team untrod,
Hath took no print of the approaching light,
And all the spangled host keep watch in squadrons
    bright?

See how from far upon the Eastern road
The star-led Wisards haste with odours sweet!
Oh! run; prevent them with thy humble ode,
And lay it lowly at his blessèd feet;
Have thou the honour first thy Lord to greet,
And join thy voice unto the Angel Quire,
From out his secret altar touched with hallowed fire.

It was the winter wild,
While the heaven-born child
All meanly wrapt in the rude manger lies;
Nature, in awe to him,
Had doffed her gaudy trim,
With her great Master so to sympathize:
It was no season then for her
To wanton with the Sun, her lusty Paramour [. . .]

But he, her fears to cease,
Sent down the meek-eyed Peace:
She, crowned with olive green, came softly sliding
Down through the turning sphere,
His ready Harbinger,
With turtle wing the amorous clouds dividing;
And, waving wide her myrtle wand,
She strikes a universal peace through sea and land [. . .]

Ring out, ye crystal spheres!
Once bless our human ears,
If ye have power to touch our senses so;
And let your silver chime
Move in melodious time;
And let the bass of heaven's deep organ blow;
And with your ninefold harmony
Make up full consort of the angelic symphony.

For, if such holy song
Enwrap our fancy long,
Time will run back and fetch the Age of Gold;
And speckled Vanity
Will sicken soon and die,
And leprous Sin will melt from earthly mould;
And Hell itself will pass away,
And leave her dolorous mansions of the peering day.

Yes, Truth and Justice then
Will down return to men,
The enamelled arras of the rainbow wearing;
And Mercy set between,
Throned in celestial sheen,
With radiant feet the tissued clouds down steering;
And Heaven, as at some festival,
Will open wide the gates of her high palace-hall.

Hark the Herald Angels Sing

from *It's Not Too Late*, A. A. Milne

Normally we spent the Christmas holidays in London. We
didn't hang up stockings on Christmas Eve. Somebody – at first
supposed to be Father Christmas, but at a very early age identi-
fied as Papa – came into our room at night, and put our presents
at the foot of the bed. It was exciting waking up in the morning
and seeing what treasure we had got; it was maddening to know
that we should not be able to enjoy them properly until we had
come back from church. Was it really supposed that a child, with
all his Christmas presents waiting for him, could give his mind
to the herald angels?

Hark the herald angels sing
(I've never had a paint-box with tubes in before)
Glory to the new-born King
(I'll paint a little cottage with a green front door)
Peace on earth and mercy mild
(My knife's a jolly good one, they've marked it Sheffield
    steel)

God and sinners reconciled
(I've got it in my pocket, I can feel it when I feel)
Hark the herald angels sing
(I wish it were tomorrow, I must sail my boat)
Glory to the new-born King
(I'll take it to the bathroom and just watch it float)

Christmas Day Sermon

Hugh Latimer

Hugh Latimer (1487–1555) was Bishop of Worcester before the Reformation, and later Church of England chaplain to King Edward VI. He was burnt at the stake by Bloody Mary. Here, edited by Nigel Rees, is an extract from one of his Christmas sermons.

To show themselves obedient, came Joseph and Mary unto Bethlehem; a long journey, and poor folks, and peradventure on foot; for we read of no great horses that she had, as our great ladies have nowadays; for truly she had no such jolly gear . . .

Well, she was great with child, and was now come to Bethlehem, where they could get never a lodging in no inn, and so were compelled to lie in a stable; and there Mary, the mother of Christ, brought forth that blessed child . . . and there 'she wrapped Him in swaddling clothes and laid Him in a manger, because there was no room for them at the inn.' For the innkeepers took only those who were able to pay for their good cheer; they would not meddle with such beggarly folk as Joseph and Mary his wife were . . .

But I warrant you, there was many a jolly damsel at that time in Bethlehem, yet amongst them all there was not one found that would humble herself so much as once to go and see poor Mary in the stable, and to comfort her. No, no; they were too fine to take so much pains, I warrant you, they had bracelets and vardingales; like as there be many nowadays amongst us, which study nothing else but how they may desire fine raiment; and in the mean season they suffer poor Mary to lie in the stable . . .

But what was her swaddling-clothes wherein she laid the King of heaven and earth? No doubt it was poor gear; peradventure it was her kercher which she took from her head, or such like gear; for I think Mary had not much fine linen; she was not trimmed up as our women be nowadays; for in the old time women were content with honest and single garments. Now they have found out these round-a-bouts; they were not invented then; the devil was not so cunning to make such gear, he found it out afterward.

Here is a question to be moved. Who fetched water to wash the child after it was born into the world, and who made a fire? It is like that Joseph did such things; for, as I told you before, those fine damsels thought it scorn to do any such thing unto Mary.

But, I pray you, to whom was the Nativity of Christ first opened? To the bishops, or great lords which were at that time at Bethlehem? Or to those jolly damsels with their vardingales, with their round-a-bouts, or with their bracelets? No, no: they had so many lets to trim and dress themselves, that they could have no time to hear of the Nativity of Christ.

But his nativity was narrated first to the shepherds . . .

Christmas with Lady Bobbin

from *Christmas Pudding*, Nancy Mitford

Christmas Day itself was organized by Lady Bobbin with the thoroughness and attention to detail of a general leading his army into battle. Not one moment of its enjoyment was left to chance or to the ingenuity of her guests; these received on Christmas Eve their marching orders, orders which must be obeyed to the letter on pain of death. Even Lady Bobbin, however, superwoman though she might be, could not prevent the day from being marked by a good deal of crossness, much over-eating, and a series of startling incidents.

The battle opened, as it were, with the Christmas stockings. These, in thickest worsted, bought specially for the occasion, were handed to the guests just before bedtime on Christmas Eve, with instructions that they were to be hung up on their bedposts by means of huge safety pins, which were also distributed. Lady Bobbin and her confederate, Lord Leamington Spa, then allowed a certain time to elapse until, judging that Morpheus would have descended upon the household, they sallied forth together (he arrayed in a white wig, beard and eyebrows and red dressing-gown, she clasping a large basket full of suitable presents) upon a stealthy noctambulation, during the course of which every stocking was neatly filled. The objects thus distributed were exactly the same every year, a curious and wonderful assortment including a pocket handkerchief, Old Moores Almanack, a balloon not as yet blown up, a mouth organ, a ball of string, a penknife, an instrument for taking stones out of horses' shoes, a book of jokes, a puzzle, and, deep down in the woolly toe of the stocking, whence it would emerge in a rather hairy condition, a chocolate baby. Alas! Most of Lady Bobbin's guests felt that they would willingly have forgone these delightful but inexpensive objects in return for the night's sleep of which they were thus deprived. Forewarned though they were, the shadowy and terrifying appearance of Lord Leamington Spa fumbling about the foot of their beds in the light of a flickering candle gave most of them such a fearful start that all thoughts of sleep were banished for many hours to come.

For the lucky ones who did manage to doze off a rude shock was presently in store. At about five o'clock in the morning Master Christopher Robin Chadlington made a tour of the bedrooms, and having awoken each occupant in turn with a blast of his mouth organ, announced in a voice fraught with tragedy that Auntie Gloria had forgotten to put a chocolate baby in his stocking. Please might I have a bit of yours? This quaint ruse was only too successful, and Christopher Robin acquired thereby no fewer than fourteen chocolate babies, all of which he ate before breakfast. The consequences, which were appalling, took place under the dining-room table at a moment when everybody else was busily opening the Christmas post. After this, weak but cheerful, young Master Chadlington spent the rest of the day in bed practising on his mouth organ.

By luncheon time any feelings of Christmas goodwill which the day and the religious service, duly attended by all, might have been expected to produce had quite evaporated, and towards the end of that meal the dining room echoed with sounds of furious argument among the grown-ups. It was the duchess who began it. She said, in a clear, ringing voice which she knew must penetrate to the consciousness of Lady Bobbin:

'Yes, the day of the capitalist is over now; and a jolly good thing too.'

'May I ask,' said Lady Bobbin, rising like a trout to this remark and leaning across the projecting stomach of Lord Leamington

Spa, 'why you, of all people, think that a good thing? Mind you, I don't admit that the capitalist system has come to an end, of course it hasn't, but why should you pretend to be pleased if it did? Affectation, I should call it.'

'No, not entirely affectation, Gloria darling. What I mean is that if, in a few years' time, people like us have no money left for luxuries we shall all, as a consequence, lead simpler and better lives. More fresh air, more sleep, more time to think and read. No night clubs, no Ritz, no Blue Train, less rushing about. And the result of that will be that we shall all be much happier. Don't you agree?'

Lady Bobbin, whose life was quite innocent of night clubs, the Ritz, and the Blue Train, and who had more time than she wanted in which to think and read, was not impressed by this statement. 'It has never been necessary to make a fool of oneself just because one happens to have money. There have always been plenty of decent people in the world, but unfortunately nobody ever hears about them, because they dont advertise themselves like the others. I wonder, Louisa, whether you will be quite so glad of the end of capitalism when you find yourself without the common necessities of life.'

'I don't anticipate that,' said the duchess comfortably. 'The world at present is suffering from over-production, not under-production, of the necessities of life.'

'Surely, duchess,' began Captain Chadlington ponderously, from his end of the table, feeling that now, if ever, was the time to make use of the information that he had so laboriously garnered from the PM, the FO, the ILP, SB, LG, and his fellow MPs, and to assert himself as a rising young politician. The duchess, however, took no notice of him and continued to goad Lady Bobbin.

'Think,' she said, 'how splendid it will be for our characters as a class if we are forced to lead simple, healthy lives, to look after our own children, and to earn our own bread. And then think of all the horrors that will be done away with, all those ghastly hideous country houses everywhere that will be pulled down. We shall be able to live in darling clean little cottages instead –'

'My house,' said Lady Bobbin, always quick to take offence, 'is, I hope, scrupulously kept. If you are implying—'

'Darling, don't be absurd. I only meant that they would be spiritually clean.'

'If you feel like this, Louisa,' said Lord Leamington Spa, now entering the lists with the light of battle in his eye, 'why on earth don't you act accordingly? Why not shut up Brackenhampton and live in one of the cottages there instead? I don't suppose there's anything to prevent you.'

'Nothing to prevent me, indeed!' cried the duchess. She had been waiting for this argument to be produced like a cat waiting for a mouse. 'There are nearly a hundred living souls to prevent me, that's all. D'you realize that we employ altogether ninety-eight people in the house and gardens at Brackenhampton? I can't, for no reason at all, take a step which would deprive all those old friends of work, food, even of a shelter over their heads. It would be quite unthinkable. I only say that if the whole system by which we live at present were to be changed we ourselves would all be a good deal happier than we are, and better in every way.'

Lady Bobbin said 'Pooh!' and rose to leave the table. She was trembling with fury.

The afternoon was so wet and foggy, so extremely unseasonable, in fact, that Lady Bobbin was obliged with the utmost reluctance to abandon the paper chase which she had organized. Until four o'clock, therefore, the house party was left to enjoy in peace that exquisite discomfort which can only be produced by overfed slumberings in armchairs. At four punctually everybody assembled in the ballroom while for nearly an hour the Woodford schoolchildren mummed. It was the

Woodford schoolchildren's annual burden to mum at Christmas; it was the annual burden of the inhabitants of Compton Bobbin to watch the mumming. Both sides, however, bore this infliction with fortitude, and no further awkwardness took place until after tea, when Lord Leamington Spa, having donned once more his dressing-gown and wig, was distributing gifts from the laden branches of the Christmas Tree. This was the big moment of the day. The tree, of course, immediately caught fire, but this was quite an usual occurrence, and the butler had no difficulty in putting it out. The real crisis occurred when Lady Bobbin opened the largish, square parcel which had 'To darling Mummy from her very loving little Bobby' written on it, and which to Lady Bobbin's rage and horror was found to contain a volume entitled *The Sexual Life of Savages in Northern Melanesia*. This classic had been purchased at great expense by poor Bobby as a present for Paul, and had somehow changed places with *Tally Ho! Songs of Horse and Hound*, which was intended for his mother, and which, unluckily, was a volume of very similar size and shape. Bobby, never losing his head for an instant, explained volubly and in tones of utmost distress to his mother and the company in general that the shop must have sent the wrong book by mistake, and this explanation was rather ungraciously accepted. Greatly to Bobby's disgust, however, *The Sexual Life of Savages in Northern Melanesia* was presently consigned to the stoke-hole flames by Lady Bobbin in person.

The remaining time before dinner, which was early so that the children could come down, was spent by Bobby and Héloïse rushing about the house in a state of wild excitement. Paul suspected, and rightly as it turned out, that this excess of high spirits boded no good to somebody. It was quite obvious to the student of youthful psychology that some practical joke was on hand. He wondered rather nervously where the blow would fall.

It fell during dinner. Captain Chadlington was in the middle of telling Lady Bobbin what the PM had said to him about pig-breeding in the West of England when a loud whirring noise was heard under his chair. He looked down, rather startled, turned white to the lips at what he saw, sprang to his feet and said, in a voice of unnatural calm: 'Will the women and children please leave the room immediately. There is an infernal machine under my chair.' A moment of panic ensued. Bobby and Héloïse, almost too swift to apprehend his meaning, rushed to the door shrieking, 'A bomb, a bomb, we shall all be blown up', while everyone else stood transfixed with horror, looking at the small black box under Captain Chadlington's chair as though uncertain of what they should do next. Paul alone remained perfectly calm.

With great presence of mind he advanced towards the box, picked it up and conveyed it to the pantry sink, where he left it with the cold water tap running over it. This golden deed made him, jointly with Captain Chadlington, the hero of the hour. Lady Bobbin shook hands with him and said he was a very plucky young fellow and had saved all their lives, and he was overwhelmed with thanks and praise on every side. Captain Chadlington, too, was supposed to have shown wonderful fortitude in requesting the women and children to leave the room before mentioning his own danger. Only Bobby and Héloïse received no praise from anybody for their behaviour and were, indeed, more or less, sent to Coventry for the rest of the evening.

Captain Chadlington, secretly delighted to think that he was now of such importance politically that attempts were made on his life (he never doubted for a moment that this was the doing of Bolshevik agents) went off to telephone to the police. Bobby and Héloïse, listening round the corner, heard him say: 'Hullo, Woodford police? It is Captain Chadlington, MP, speaking from Compton Bobbin. Look here, officer, there has just been an attempt to assassinate me. The Bolsheviks, I suppose. An infernal machine under my chair at dinner. Would you send somebody along to examine it at once, please, and inform Scotland Yard of what has happened?'

Lady Brenda said: 'I have always been afraid of something like this ever since Charlie made that speech against Bolshevism at Moreton-in-Marsh. Anyhow, we must be thankful that it was no worse.'

Lady Bobbin said that perhaps now the Government would do something about the Bolsheviks at last. Lord Leamington Spa said that he didn't like it at all, which was quite true, he didn't, because on Christmas night after dinner he always sang 'The Mistletoe Bough' with great feeling and now it looked as though the others would be too busy talking about the bomb to listen to him. Michael Lewes and Squibby Almanack dared to wonder whether it was really an infernal machine at all, but they only imparted this scepticism to each other. The duchess said that of course it would be very good publicity for Charlie Chadlington, and she wondered – but added that perhaps, on the whole, he was too stupid to think of such a thing. Captain Chadlington said that public men must expect this sort of thing and that he didn't mind for himself, but that it was just like those cowardly dagoes to attempt to blow up a parcel of women and children as well.

Everybody agreed that the tutor had behaved admirably.

'Where did you get it from?' Paul asked Bobby, whom he presently found giggling in the schoolroom with the inevitable Héloïse.

'A boy in my house made it for me last half; he says nobody will be able to tell that it's not a genuine bomb. In fact, it is a genuine one, practically; that's the beauty of it. Poor old Charlie Chad., he's most awfully pleased about the whole thing, isn't he, fussing about with those policemen like any old turkey cock. Oh! It all went off too, too beautifully, I couldn't think it funnier, could you?'

'I think you're an odious child,' said Paul, 'and I've a very good mind to tell your mother about you.'

'That would rather take the gilt off your heroic action, though, wouldn't it, old boy?' said Bobby comfortably.

The local police, as Bobby's friend had truly predicted, were unable to make up their minds as to whether the machine was or was not an infernal one. Until this pretty point should be settled Captain Chadlington was allotted two human bulldogs who were instructed by Scotland Yard that they must guard his life with their own. A camp bed was immediately made up for one of these trusty fellows in the passage, across the captain's bedroom door, and the other was left to prowl about the house and garden all night, armed to the teeth.

'Darling,' said the duchess to Bobby, as they went upstairs to bed after this exhausting day, 'have you seen the lovely man who's sleeping just outside my room? I don't know what your mother expects to happen, but one is only made of flesh and blood after all.'

'Well, for goodness sake, try and remember that you're a duchess again now,' said Bobby, kissing his aunt good night.

The Mistletoe Bough

Thomas Haynes Bayly

The mistletoe hung in the castle hall
The holly branch shone on the old oak wall.
The Baron's retainers were blithe and gay,
Keeping the Christmas holiday.
The Baron beheld with a father's pride
His beautiful child, Lord Lovell's bride.

And she, with her bright eyes seemed to be
The star of that goodly company.

'I'm weary of dancing, now,' she cried;
'Here, tarry a moment, I'll hide, I'll hide,
And, Lovell, be sure you're the first to trace
The clue to my secret hiding place.'
Away she ran, and her friends began
Each tower to search and each nook to scan.
And young Lovell cried, 'Oh, where do you hide?
I'm lonesome without you, my own fair bride.'

They sought her that night, they sought her next day,
They sought her in vain when a week passed away.
In the highest, the lowest, the loneliest spot,
Young Lovell sought wildly, but found her not.
The years passed by and their brief at last
Was told as a sorrowful tale long past.
When Lovell appeared, all the children cried,
'See the old man weeps for his fairy bride.'

At length, an old chest that had long laid hid
Was found in the castle; they raised the lid.
A skeleton form lay mouldering there
In the bridal wreath of that lady fair.
How sad the day when in sportive jest
She hid from her lord in the old oak chest,
It closed with a spring and a dreadful doom,
And the bride lay clasped in a living tomb.

Dolphins in the Thames

from *Annales, or a General Chronicle of England*, John Stow

AD 1392– King Richard with Queene Anne his wife, foure bishops, as many Earles, the Duke of Yorke, many Lords, and fifteen Ladies held a royall Christmas at Langley neere to St Albans. The same Christmas Day a Dolphin came foorth of the Sea and played himself in ye Thames at London to the bridge, foreshewing happily the tempests that were to follow within a week after, the which Dolphin being seene of the Citizens, and followed, was with much difficulty the Citizens, and followed, was with much difficulty intercepted, and brought againe to London, shewing a spectacle to many, of the height of his body, for hee was ten foote in length. These Dolphins are fishes of the Sea that follow the voices of men, and rejoice in the playing of instruments & are wont to gather themselves at musicke. These when they play in rivers, with hasty springings or leapings doe signifie Tempest to follow. The Seas containe nothing more swift nor nimble, for sometimes with their skips, they mount over the sailes of ships.

The Glastonbury Thorn

from *The World*, Adam Fitz-Adam

The Glastonbury Thorn, a form of common hawthorn, is said to have flowered on Wearyall Hill, Somerset, every Christmas day for 2,000 years, since Joseph of Arimathea thrust the staff he brought from the Holy Land into the soil and it miraculously broke into blossom.

My readers, no doubt, are already aware that I have in my eye the wonderful thorn of Glastonbury, which though hitherto regarded as a trunk of popish imposture, has notably exerted itself as the most protestant plant in the universe. It is well known that the correction of the Calendar was enacted by Pope Gregory the Thirteenth, and that the reformed Churches have, with a proper spirit of opposition, adhered to the old calculation of the Emperor Julius Cæsar, who was by no means a papist. Near two years ago the Popish Calendar was brought in (I hope by persons well affected). Certain it is that the Glastonbury Thorn has preserved its inflexibility, and observed its old anniversary. Many thousand spectators visited it on the parliamentary Christmas Day – not a bud was to be seen! – On the true Nativity it was covered with blossoms. One must be an infidel indeed to spurn at such authority. Had I been consulted [. . .] instead of turning the calendar topsy-turvey, by fantastic calculations, I should have proposed to regulate the year by the infallible Somersetshire thorn, and to have reckoned the months from Christmas-day, which should always have been kept as the Glastonbury thorn should blow.

Many inconveniences, to be sure, would follow from this system; but as holy things ought to be the first consideration of a religious nation, the inconvenicences should be overlooked. The thorn can never blow but on the true Christmas-day; and consequently, the apprehension of the year's becoming inverted by sticking to the Julian account can never hold. If the course of the sun varies, astronomers may find out some way to adjust that: but it is preposterous, not to say presumptuous, to be celebrating Christmas-day when the Glastonbury thorn, which certainly must know times and seasons better than an almanack-maker, declares it to be heresy.

Fine Old Christmas

from *The Mill on the Floss*, George Eliot

Fine old Christmas, with the snowy hair and ruddy face, had done his duty that year in the noblest fashion, and had set off his rich gifts of warmth and colour with all the heightening contrast of frost and snow.

Snow lay on the croft and riverbank in undulations softer than the limbs of infancy; it lay with the neatliest finished border on every sloping roof, making the dark-red gables stand out with a new depth of colour; it weighed heavily on the laurels and fir trees, till it fell from them with a shuddering sound; it clothed the rough turnip field with whiteness, and made the sheep look like dark blotches; the gates were all blocked up with the sloping drifts, and here and there a disregarded four-footed beast stood as if petrified 'in unrecumbent sadness'; there was no gleam, no shadow, for the heavens, too, were one still, pale cloud; no sound or motion in anything but the dark river that flowed and moaned like an unresting sorrow. But old Christmas smiled as he laid this cruel-seeming spell on the outdoor world, for he meant to light up home with new brightness, to deepen all the richness of indoor colour, and give a keener edge of delight to the warm fragrance of food; he meant to prepare a sweet imprisonment that would strengthen the primitive fellow-ship of kindred, and make the sunshine of familiar human faces as welcome as the hidden day-star. His kindness fell but hardly on the homeless – fell but hardly on the homes where the hearth was not very warm, and where the food had little fragrance; where the human faces had had no sunshine in them, but rather the leaden, blank-eyed gaze of unexpectant want. But the fine old season meant well; and if he has not learned the secret how to bless men impartially, it is because his father Time, with ever-unrelenting unrelenting purpose, still hides that secret in his own mighty, slow-beating heart.

And yet this Christmas day, in spite of Tom's fresh delight in home, was not, he thought, somehow or other, quite so happy as it had always been before. The red berries were just as abundant on the holly, and he and Maggie had dressed all the windows and mantelpieces and picture frames on Christmas Eve with as much taste as ever, wedding the thick-set scarlet clusters with branches of the black-berried ivy. There had been singing under the windows after midnight – supernatural singing, Maggie always felt, in spite of Tom's contemptuous insistence that the singers were old Patch, the parish clerk, and the rest of the church choir; she trembled with awe when their carolling broke in upon her dreams, and the image of men in fustian clothes was always thrust away by the vision of angels resting on the parted cloud. The midnight chant had helped as usual to lift the morning above the level of common days; and then there were the smell of hot toast and ale from the kitchen, at the breakfast hour; the favourite anthem, the green boughs, and the short sermon gave the appropriate festal character to the church-going; and aunt and uncle Moss, with all their seven children, were looking like so many reflectors of the bright parlour fire, when the church-goers came back, stamping the snow from their feet. The plum pudding was of the same handsome roundness as ever, and came in with the symbolic blue flames around it, as if it had been heroically snatched from the nether fires, into which it had been thrown by dyspeptic Puritans; the dessert was as splendid as ever, with its golden oranges, brown nuts, and the crystalline light and dark of apple jelly and damson cheese; in all these things Christmas was as it had always been since Tom could remember; it was only distinguished, it by anything, by superior sliding and snowballs.

Letter from the Trenches

Albert Downes

Little Grey Home
Watery Lane
Xmasday *1914*

My own darling girl,

Had your two letters and two letter cards posted from Sydney this morning and was glad to get them, well old girl here we are Xmas day in the trenches of course it's rather difficult to realise that it is Christmas except that we had an order over the 'phone this morning that-no firing was to take place at all unless absolutely necessary & now there is hardly a shot fired by them and it sounds almost peaceful. My fellows have been singing carols & so have the Germans however I've just warned my Sentries to be extra on the look out because I don't trust 'em a yard. What say you? I've had a fireplace dug in the trench wall opposite my hut & have a blazing log fire going. Our fellows got the logs last night a perilous job but worth it and so I've been sitting down and gazing into the flames thinking of you and my people at home & picturing your doings as far as I can. We are being relieved this evening & are going to keep Xmas properly as far as we can in Billets . . . I meant to have finished this and posted it Xmas Day but I was stopped by being informed that about *100* Germans had got out of their trenches in front of my company I suppose they knew we wouldn't fire at them and were burying their dead. There are heaps about half way between – of course I thought they must be up to some game, digging new trenches or something so I sent a few of my fellows out to see – they walked up to the groups shook hands & chatted in a most friendly way for quite an hour. Of course none of the men who were out had any arms or should have fired at them. Quite a lot of their men could talk English well & said they were all pretty fed up & hoped the war would soon be over – they exchanged cigarettes & souvenirs & c & then they all went back & so did our chaps. It was a most peculiar sight I can assure [you] & I don't expect you will believe me but it is an honest fact Cissie.

Christmas Day in the Workhouse
George R. Simms

It is Christmas Day in the workhouse,
And the cold, bare walls are bright
With garlands of green and holly,
And the place is a pleasant sight;
For with clean-washed hands and faces,
In a long and hungry line
The paupers sit at the table,
For this is the hour they dine.

And the guardians and their ladies,
Although the wind is east,
Have come in their furs and wrappers,
To watch their charges feast;
To smile and be condescending,
Put pudding on pauper plates.
To be hosts at the workhouse banquet
They've paid for – with the rates.

Oh, the paupers are meek and lowly
With their 'Thank'ee kindly, mum's!'
So long as they fill their stomachs,
What matter it whence it comes!
But one of the old men mutters,
And pushes his plate aside:
'Great God!' he cries, 'but it chokes me!
For this is the day she died!'

The guardians gazed in horror,
The master's face went white;
'Did a pauper refuse the pudding?'
'Could their ears believe aright?'
Then the ladies clutched their husbands,
Thinking the man would die,
Struck by a bolt, or something,
By the outraged One on high.

But the pauper sat for a moment,
Then rose 'mid silence grim,
For the others had ceased to chatter
And trembled in every limb.
He looked at the guardians' ladies,
Then, eyeing their lords, he said,
'I eat not the food of villains
Whose hands are foul and red:

'Whose victims cry for vengeance
From their dark, unhallowed graves.'
'He's drunk!' said the workhouse master,
'Or else he's mad and raves.'
'Not drunk or mad,' cried the pauper,
'But only a haunted beast,
Who, torn by the hounds and mangled,
Declines the vulture's feast.

'I care not a curse for the guardians,
And I won't be dragged away;
Just let me have the fit out,
It's only on Christmas Day
That the black past comes to goad me,
And prey on my burning brain;
I'll tell you the rest in a whisper –
I swear I won't shout again.

'Keep your hands off me, curse you!
Hear me right out to the end.
You come here to see how paupers
The season of Christmas spend;
You come here to watch us feeding,
As they watched the captured beast.
Here's why a penniless pauper
Spits on your paltry feast.

'Do you think I will take your bounty,
And let you smile and think
You're doing a noble action
With the parish's meat and drink?
Where is my wife, you traitors –
The poor old wife you slew?
Yes, by the God above me,
My Nance was killed by you!

'Last winter my wife lay dying,
Starved in a filthy den;
I had never been to the parish –
I came to the parish then.
I swallowed my pride in coming,
For ere the ruin came,
I held up my head as a trader,
And I bore a spotless name.

'I came to the parish, craving
Bread for a starving wife,
Bread for the woman who'd loved me
Through fifty years of life;
And what do you think they told me,
Mocking my awful grief,
That "the House" was open to us,
But they wouldn't give "out relief".

'I slunk to the filthy alley –
'Twas a cold, raw Christmas Eve –
And the bakers' shops were open,
Tempting a man to thieve;
But I clenched my fists together,
Holding my head awry,
So I came to her empty-handed
And mournfully told her why.

'Then I told her the house was open;
She had heard of the ways of that,
For her bloodless cheeks went crimson,
and up in her rags she sat,
Crying, "Bide the Christmas here, John,
We've never had one apart;
I think I can bear the hunger –
The other would break my heart."

'All through that eve I watched her,
Holding her hand in mine,
Praying the Lord and weeping,
Till my lips were salt as brine;
I asked her once if she hungered,
And as she answered "No",
The moon shone in at the window,
Set in a wreath of snow.

'Then the room was bathed in glory,
And I saw in my darling's eyes
The faraway look of wonder
That comes when the spirit flies;
And her lips were parched and parted,
And her reason came and went.
For she raved of our home in Devon,
Where our happiest years were spent.

'And the accents, long forgotten,
Came back to the tongue once more.
For she talked like the country lassie
I woo'd by the Devon shore;
Then she rose to her feet and trembled,
And fell on the rags and moaned,
And, "Give me a crust – I'm famished –
For the love of God!" she groaned.

'I rushed from the room like a madman
And flew to the workhouse gate,
Crying, "Food for a dying woman!"
And the answer came, "Too late."
They drove me away with curses;
Then I fought with a dog in the street
And tore from the mongrel's clutches
A crust he was trying to eat.

'Back through the filthy byways!
Back through the trampled slush!
Up to the crazy garret,
Wrapped in an awful hush;
My heart sank down at the threshold,
And I paused with a sudden thrill.
For there, in the silv'ry moonlight,
My Nance lay, cold and still.

'Up to the blackened ceiling,
The sunken eyes were cast –
I knew on those lips, all bloodless,
My name had been the last;
She called for her absent husband –
O God! had I but known! –
Had called in vain, and, in anguish,
Had died in that den – alone.

'Yes, there, in a land of plenty,
Lay a loving woman dead,
Cruelly starved and murdered
for a loaf of the parish bread;
At yonder gate, last Christmas,
I craved for a human life,
You, who would feed us paupers,
What of my murdered wife!

'There, get ye gone to your dinners,
Don't mind me in the least,
Think of the happy paupers
Eating your Christmas feast;
And when you recount their blessings
In your smug parochial way,
Say what you did for me, too,
Only last Christmas Day.'

Christmas with the Pooters

from *The Diary of a Nobody*,
George and Weedon Grossmith

December 24 – I am a poor man, but I would gladly give ten shillings to find out who sent me the insulting Christmas card I received this morning. I never insult people; why should they insult me? The worst part of the transaction is, that I find myself suspecting all of my friends. The handwriting on the envelope is evidently disguised, being written sloping the wrong way. I cannot think either Gowing or Cummings would do such a mean thing. Lupin denied all knowledge of it, and I believe him; although I disapprove of his laughing and sympathizing with the offender. Mr Franching would be above such an act; and I don't think any of the Mutlars would descent to such a course. I wonder if Pitt, that impudent clerk at the office, did it? Or Mrs Birrell, the charwoman, or Burwin-Fosselton? The writing is too good for the former.

Christmas Day – We caught the 10.20 train at Paddington, and spent a pleasant day at Carrie's mother's. The country was quite nice and pleasant, although the roads were sloppy. We dined in the middle of the day, just ten of us, and talked over old times. If everybody had a nice, *un*interfering mother-in-law, such as I have, what a deal of happiness there would be in the world. Being all in good spirits, I proposed her health, and I made, I think, a very good speech.

I concluded, rather neatly, by saying: 'On an occasion like this – whether relatives, friends, or acquaintances – we are all inspired with good feelings towards each other. We are of one mind, and think only of love and friendship. Those who have quarrelled with absent friends should kiss and make it up. Those who happily have not fallen out, can kiss all the same.'

I saw the tears in the eyes of both Carrie and her mother, and must say I felt very flattered by the compliment. That dear old Reverend John Panzy Smith, who married us, made a most cheerful and amusing speech, and said he should act on my suggestion respecting the kissing. He then walked round the table and kissed all the ladies, including Carrie. Of course one did not object to this; but I was more than staggered when a young fellow named Moss, who was a stranger to me, and who had scarcely spoken a word through dinner, jumped up suddenly with a sprig of mistletoe, and exclaimed: 'Hulloh! I don't see why I shouldn't be on in this scene.' Before one could realise what he was about to do, he kissed Carrie and the rest of the ladies.

Fortunately the matter was treated as a joke, and we all laughed; but it was a dangerous experiment, and I felt very uneasy for a moment as to the result. I subsequently referred to the matter to Carrie, but she said: 'Oh, he's not much more than a boy.' I said that he had a very large moustache for a boy. Carrie replied: 'I didn't say he was not a nice boy.'

December 26 – I did not sleep very well last night; I never do in a strange bed. I feel a little indigestion, which one must expect at this time of the year. Carrie and I returned to Town in the evening. Lupin came in late. He said he enjoyed his Christmas, and added: 'I feel as fit as a Lowther Arcade fiddle, and only require a little more 'oof to feel as fit as a 500 pounds Stradivarius.' I have long since given up trying to understand Lupin's slang, or asking him to explain it.

December 27 – I told Lupin I was expecting Gowing and Cummings to drop in tomorrow evening for a quiet game. I was in hope the boy would volunteer to stay in, and help to amuse them. Instead of which, he said: 'Oh, you had better put them off, as I have asked Daisy and Frank Mutlar to come.' I said I could not think of doing such a thing. Lupin said: 'Then I will send a wire, and put off Daisy.' I suggested that a postcard or letter would reach her quite soon enough, and would not be so extravagant.

Carrie, who had listened to the above conversation with apparent annoyance, directed a well-aimed shaft at Lupin. She said: 'Lupin, why do you object to Daisy meeting your father's friends? Is it because they are not good enough for her, or (which is equally possible) *she* is not good enough for them?' Lupin was dumbfounded, and could make no reply. When he left the room, I gave Carrie a kiss of approval.

December 28 – Lupin, on coming down to breakfast, said to his mother: 'I have not put off Daisy and Frank, and should like them to join Gowing and Cummings this evening.' I felt very pleased with the boy for this. Carrie said, in reply: 'I am glad you let me know in time, as I can turn over the cold leg of mutton, dress it with a little parsley, and no one will know it has been cut.' She further said she would make a few custards, and stew some pippins, so that they would be cold by the evening.

Finding Lupin in good spirits, I asked him quietly if he really had any personal objection to either Gowing or Cummings. He replied: 'Not in the least. I think Cummings looks rather an ass, but that is partly due to his patronising "the three-and-six-one-price hat company", and wearing a reach-me-down frock-coat. As for that perpetual brown velveteen jacket of Gowing's – why, he resembles an itinerant photographer.'

I said it was not the coat that made the gentleman; where-upon Lupin, with a laugh, replied: 'No, and it wasn't much of a gentleman who made their coats.'

We were rather jolly at supper, and Daisy made herself very agreeable, especially in the earlier part of the evening, when she sang. At supper, however, she said: 'Can you make tee-to-tums with bread?' and she commenced rolling up pieces of bread, and twisting them round on the table. I felt this to be bad manners, but of course said nothing. Presently Daisy and Lupin, to my disgust, began throwing bread-pills at each other. Frank followed suit, and so did Cummings and Gowing, to my astonishment. They then commenced throwing hard pieces of crust, one piece catching me on the forehead, and making me blink. I said: 'Steady, please; steady!' Frank jumped up and said: 'Tum, tum; then the band played.'

I did not know what this meant, but they all roared, and continued the bread-battle. Gowing suddenly seized all the parsley off the cold mutton, and threw it full in my face. I looked daggers at Gowing, who replied: 'I say, it's no good trying to look indignant, with your hair full of parsley.' I rose from the table, and insisted that a stop should be put to this foolery at once. Frank Mutlar shouted: 'Time, gentlemen, please! time!' and turned out the gas, leaving us in absolute darkness.

I was feeling my way out of the room, when I suddenly received a hard intentional punch at the back of my head. I said loudly: 'Who did that?' There was no answer; so I repeated the question, with the same result. I struck a match, and lighted the gas. They were all talking and laughing, so I kept my own counsel; but, after they had gone, I said to Carrie; 'The person who sent me that insulting postcard at Christmas was here tonight.'

A Disappointing Christmas Dinner

from the diary of Captain H. F. G Malet

Harry Malet served with 4th Pahang Battalion, Federated Malay States Volunteer Force during the Malayan campaign. Having moved his family to Cape Town when hostilities seemed likely, Captain H. Malet was captured when Singapore fell. He was later sent to work on the infamous Burma Railway and died in Kanyu on 4 June 1943. His diary was returned to his wife after the war. On Christmas Day 1942 he was at No. 3 River Camp, Kanyu.

It is now *12.30* as I write and I have just come back from our Morning Service. The 'Church' – the clearing in the bamboo jungle overlooking the river – the latter flowing some *50* to *70* feet below us. The Altar is a large boulder, and behind is a bamboo cross about *5* feet tall. There must have been about *150* to *200* in Church – i.e. sitting in rows up the hillside, and Padre Parr preached quite adequately. At *8.30* I went to Holy Communion at which there were over *100* Communicants and very beautiful it was. The early sun coming through the morning mist and shining on the river and opposite jungle-clad hills – the real time being *6.30* of course. The early bird songs in the trees around us and the old accustomed monkey calls 'Wah-Wah's' being the most prevalent. A small flight of giant toucans flew over and the wild peacocks called to each other stridently – as I say – a really jungle setting for our Christmas Communion, with the *14* little white crosses of our cemetery beside us. As we waited for the Service to begin – sitting on split bamboos on the ground – I worked out that Jo was then at that moment probably coming home from Midnight Mass in the glorious full moonlight.

At <u>midnight</u> last night I went to Mass – in the R.C. 'Church' – a little clearing in the bamboo jungle on the hillside between the two valleys in which our huts are built. They have a little Altar, Altar rails and side table – all fronted with ataps. Candles in bamboo sconces were lighted – incense made from jungle dammar was duly swung in a censer made from an old jam tin burnished and hung on an old dog chain, but the whole effect was perfect! . . . Father Burke gave a delightful address on the subject of our Homes and Loved Ones and, of course, my object in going was chiefly to feel I was sharing (in such amazingly different surroundings) in just such a Service as my own little family are going to or at any rate Jo will be going if she is able. This time last year we were in bivouacs in the jungle at Kemubu having just withdrawn to a defended position south of the river. I was talking to Al Hazlett after breakfast and reminding him of last Xmas when a voice came from behind us saying, 'Yes, I was there too!' It was Capt Edgar of the R.E.s – just emerged from 2 weeks in hospital with dysentery. I had not met him since Singapore before the Capitulation (another Old Cheltonian – making about half a dozen or more in this Camp!).

December 26th – Boxing Day

Yesterday we had a disappointment as our Xmas Dinner – one pig – was found to be alive with maggots and quite unfit for consumption! We had a 'pasty' made of sweet potato with our usual root jungle stew. From the canteen 5/- allowance we opened a tin of ovals between the three of us – Geoff Brown, Leslie Jerram and myself. That gave us 3½ sardines each, which added to the rice, pasty and stew, gave us our Christmas dinner – and very nice too. We are not accustomed to such richness and went to bed feeling absolutely bloated. What worries us is to think how incapable we shall be of doing justice to a real Xmas Dinner next year if we can't deal with <u>this</u> one.

The Mahogany Tree

W. M. Thackaray

Christmas is here;
Winds whistle shrill,
Icy and chill,
Little care we;

Little we fear
Weather without,
Shelter'd about
The Mahogany Tree.

Once on the boughs
Birds of rare plume
Sang, in its bloom;
Night birds are we;

Here we carouse,
Singing, like them,
Perch'd round the stem
Of the jolly old tree.

Here let us sport,
Boys, as we sit —
Laughter and wit
Flashing so free.

Life is but short —
When we are gone,
Let them sing on,
Round the old tree.

Evenings we knew,
Happy as this;
Faces we miss,
Pleasant to see.

Kind hearts and true,
Gentle and just,
Peace to your dust!
We sing round the tree.

Care, like a dun,
Lurks at the gate:
Let the dog wait;
Happy we'll be!

Drink every one;
Pile up the coals,
Fill the red bowls,
Round the old tree.

Drain we the cup —
Friend, art afraid?
Spirits are laid
In the Red Sea.

Mantle it up;
Empty it yet;
Let us forget,
Round the old tree.

Sorrows, begone!
Life and its ills,
Duns and their bills,
Bid we to flee.

Come with the dawn,
Blue-devil sprite,
Leave us to-night,
Round the old tree.

A Visit from Uncle Pumblechook

from *Great Expectations*, Charles Dickens

We were to have a superb dinner, consisting of a leg of pickled pork and greens, and a pair of roast stuffed fowls. A handsome mince pie had been made yesterday morning (which accounted for the mincemeat not being missed), and the pudding was already on the boil. These extensive arrangements occasioned us to be cut off unceremoniously in respect of breakfast; 'for I ain't', said Mrs Joe – 'I ain't a going to have no formal cramming and busting and washing up now, with what I've got before me, I promise you!'

So, we had our slices served out, as if we were two thousand troops on a forced march instead of a man and boy at home; and we took gulps of milk and water, with apologetic countenances, from a jug on the dresser. In the meantime, Mrs Joe put clean white curtains up, and tacked a new flowered flounce across the wide chimney to replace the old one, and uncovered the little state parlour across the passage, which was never uncovered at any other time, but passed the rest of the year in a cool haze of silver paper, which even extended to the four little white crockery poodles on the mantelshelf, each with a black nose and a basket of flowers in his mouth, and each the counterpart of the other. Mrs Joe was a very clean housekeeper, but had an exquisite art of making her cleanliness more uncomfortable and unacceptable than dirt itself. Cleanliness is next to Godliness, and some people do the same by their religion.

My sister, having so much to do, was going to church vicari-ously, that is to say, Joe and I were going. In his working clothes, Joe was a well-knit characteristic-looking blacksmith; in his holiday clothes, he was more like a scarecrow in good circum-stances, than anything else. Nothing that he wore then fitted him or seemed to belong to him; and everything that he wore then grazed him. On the present festive occasion he emerged from his room, when the blithe bells were going, the picture of misery, in a full suit of Sunday penitentials. As to me, I think my sister must have had some general idea that I was a young offender whom an Accoucheur Policeman had taken up (on my birthday) and delivered over to her, to be dealt with according to the outraged majesty of the law. I was always treated as if I had insisted on being born in opposition to the dictates of reason, religion, and morality, and against the dissuading arguments of my best friends. Even when I was taken to have a new suit of clothes, the tailor had orders to make them like a kind of Reformatory, and on no account to let me have the free use of my limbs.

Joe and I going to church, therefore, must have been a moving spectacle for compassionate minds [. . .]

Mr Wopsle, the clerk at church, was to dine with us; and Mr Hubble the wheelwright and Mrs Hubble; and Uncle Pumblechook (Joe's uncle, but Mrs Joe appropriated him), who was a well-to-do corn-chandler in the nearest town, and drove his own chaise-cart. The dinner hour was half-past one. When Joe and I got home, we found the table laid, and Mrs Joe dressed, and the dinner dressing, and the front door unlocked (it never was at any other time) for the company to enter by, and everything most splendid. And still, not a word of the robbery.

The time came, without bringing with it any relief to my feelings, and the company came [. . .] 'Mrs Joe', said Uncle Pumblechook, a large hard-breathing middle-aged slow man, with a mouth like a fish, dull staring eyes, and sandy hair stand-ing upright on his head, so that he looked as if he had just been all but choked, and had that moment come to, 'I have brought you as the compliments of the season – I have brought you, Mum, a bottle of sherry wine – and I have brought you, Mum, a bottle of port wine.'

Every Christmas Day he presented himself, as a profound novelty, with exactly the same words, and carrying the two bottles like dumb-bells. Every Christmas Day, Mrs Joe replied, as she now replied, 'Oh, Un–cle Pum–ble–chook! This IS kind!' Every Christmas Day, he retorted, as he now retorted, 'It's no more than your merits. And now are you all bobbish, and how's Sixpennorth of halfpence?' meaning me.

We dined on these occasions in the kitchen, and adjourned, for the nuts and oranges and apples to the parlour; which was a change very like Joe's change from his working clothes to his Sunday dress. My sister was uncommonly lively on the present occasion, and indeed was generally more gracious in the society of Mrs Hubble than in other company. I remember Mrs Hubble as a little curly sharp-edged person in sky-blue, who held a conventionally juven-ile position, because she had married Mr Hubble – I don't know at what remote period – when she was much younger than he. I remember Mr Hubble as a tough, high-shouldered, stooping old man, of a sawdusty fragrance, with his legs extraordinarily wide apart: so that in my short days I always saw some miles of open country between them when I met him coming up the lane.

Among this good company I should have felt myself, even if I hadn't robbed the pantry, in a false position. Not because I was squeezed in at an acute angle of the tablecloth, with the table in my chest, and the Pumblechookian elbow in my eye, nor because I was not allowed to speak (I didn't want to speak), nor because I was regaled with the scaly tips of the drumsticks of the fowls, and with those obscure corners of pork of which the pig, when living, had had the least reason to be vain. No; I should not have minded that, if they would only have left me alone. But they wouldn't leave me alone. They seemed to think the opportunity lost, if they failed to point the conversation at me, every now and then, and stick the point into me. I might have been an unfortunate little bull in a Spanish arena, I got so smartingly touched up by these moral goads.

It began the moment we sat down to dinner. Mr Wopsle said grace with theatrical declamation – as it now appears to me, something like a religious cross of the Ghost in Hamlet with Richard the Third – and ended with the very proper aspiration that we might be truly grateful. Upon which my sister fixed me with her eye, and said, in a low reproachful voice, 'Do you hear that? Be grateful.'

'Especially,' said Mr Pumblechook, 'be grateful, boy, to them which brought you up by hand.'

Mrs Hubble shook her head, and contemplating me with a mournful presentiment that I should come to no good, asked, 'Why is it that the young are never grateful?' This moral mystery seemed too much for the company until Mr Hubble tersely solved it by saying, 'Naterally wicious.' Everybody then murmured 'True!' and looked at me in a particularly unpleasant and personal manner.

The Masque of Christmas

Ben Jonson

The Court being seated,
 Enter CHRISTMAS *and his children, with two or three of the guard, attired in round Hose, long Stockings, a close Doublet, a high-crowned Hat, with a Brooch, a long, thin Beard, a Truncheon, little Ruffes, white*

Shoos, his Scarfs and Garters tied cross, and his Drum beaten before him.

Why, gentlemen, do you know what you do? Ha! would you have kept me out? CHRISTMAS, old Christmas, Christmas of *London*, and Captain Christmas? Pray you, let me be brought before my Lord Chamberlain, I'll not be answered else: *'Tis merry in hall, when beards wag all.*

The Truth is, I have brought a Masque here, out o' the Citty, of my own making, and do present it by a Sett of my sons, that come out of the Lanes of *London,* good dancing Boyes all. It was intended, I confess, for *Curriers' Hall*; but because the weather has been open, and the Liverie were not at leisure to see it till a Frost came, that they cannot worke, I thought it convenient, with some little Alterations, and the Groome of the revels' hand to 't, to fit it for a higher Place; which I have done, and though I say it, another manner of device than your *New Yeares Night.* Bones o' bread, the king! *(seeing his Mjty.)* Son *Rowland!* Son *Clem!* be ready there in a Trice: quick, boyes!

Enter his SONS and DAUGHTERS, (ten in number,) led in, in a string, by CUPID, who is attired in a flat Capp, and a Prentice's Coat, with Winges at his Shoulders.

MISRULE, in a velvet Capp, with a sprig, a short Cloke, great yellow Ruff (like a Reveller) his Torche-Bearer bearing a Rope, a Cheese, and a Basket.

CAROL, a long tawny Coat, with a red Capp, and a Flute at his Girdle, his torch-bearer carrying a Song-booke open.

MINCED-PIE, like a fine Cook's wife, drest neat; her Man carrying a Pye, Dish, and Spoones.

GAMBOL, like a Tumbler, with a Hoope and Bells; his Torch-bearer armed with a Colt-staff, and a binding cloth.

POST AND PAIR, with a Pair-royal of Aces in his Hat; his garment all done over with Pairs and Purs; his 'Squire carrying a Box, Cards, and Counters.

NEW-YEARE'S-GIFT, in a blue coat, serving-man like, with

an orange, and a sprig of rosemary gilt on his head, his hat full of brooches, with a collar of ginger-bread, his torch-bearer carrying a march-pane with a bottle of wine on either arm.

MUMMING, in a masquing pied Suit, with a Vizard, his Torche-bearer carrying the Boxe, and ringing it.

WASSEL, like a neat Sempster and Songster; her Page bearing a brown Bowle, drest with Ribbands, and Rosemary before her.

OFFERING, in a short gown, with a Porter's Staffe in his Hand, a Wyth born before him, and a Bason, by his Torche-Bearer.

BABY-CAKE, drest like a Boy, in a fine long Coat, Biggin-bib, Muckender, and a little Dagger; his usher bearing a great Cake, with a Beane and a Pease.

They enter singing.

> Now God preserve, as you do well deserve,
> Your Majesties all, two there;
> Your Highnesse small, with my good Lords all,
> And Ladies, how do you do there?
>
> Give me leave to ask, for I bring you a masque
> From little, little, little London;
> Which say the king likes, I have passed the pikes,
> If not, old Christmas is undone.

Heathcliff's Christmas

from *Wuthering Heights*, Emily Bronte

After playing lady's-maid to the newcomer, and putting my cakes in the oven, and making the house and kitchen cheerful with great fires, befitting Christmas eve, I prepared to sit down and amuse myself by singing carols, all alone; regardless of Joseph's affirmations that he considered the merry tunes I chose as next door to songs.

He had retired to private prayer in his chamber, and Mr and Mrs Earnshaw were engaging Missy's attention by sundry gay trifles bought for her to present to the little Lintons, as an acknowledgment of their kindness. They had invited them to spend the morrow at Wuthering Heights, and the invitation had been accepted, on one condition: Mrs Linton begged that her darlings might be kept carefully apart from that 'naughty swearing boy.'

Under these circumstances I remained solitary. I smelt the rich scent of the heating spices; and admired the shining kitchen utensils, the polished clock, decked in holly, the silver mugs ranged on a tray ready to be filled with mulled ale for supper; and above all, the speckless purity of my particular care – the scoured and well-swept floor.

I gave due inward applause to every object, and then I remembered how old Earnshaw used to come in when all was tidied, and call me a cant lass, and slip a shilling into my hand as a Christmas-box; and from that I went on to think of his fondness for Heathcliff, and his dread lest he should suffer neglect after death had removed him: and that naturally led me to consider the poor lad's situation now, and from singing I changed my mind to crying. It struck me soon, however, there would be more sense in endeavouring to repair some of his wrongs than shedding tears over them: I got up and walked into the court to seek him.

He was not far; I found him smoothing the glossy coat of the new pony in the stable, and feeding the other beasts, according to custom.

'Make haste, Heathcliff!' I said, 'the kitchen is so comfortable; and Joseph is upstairs: make haste, and let me dress you smart before Miss Cathy comes out, and then you can sit together, with the whole hearth to yourselves, and have a long chatter till bedtime.'

He proceeded with his task, and never turned his head towards me.

'Come – are you coming?' I continued. 'There's a little cake for each of you, nearly enough; and you'll need half-an-hour's donning.'

I waited five minutes, but getting no answer left him. Catherine supped with her brother and sister-in-law: Joseph and I joined at an unsociable meal, seasoned with reproofs on one side and sauciness on the other. His cake and cheese remained on the table all night for the fairies.

A Christmas Carol

G. K. Chesterton

The Christ-child lay on Mary's lap,
His hair was like a light.
(O weary, weary were the world,
But here is all aright.)

The Christ-child lay on Mary's breast
His hair was like a star.
(O stern and cunning are the kings,
But here the true hearts are.)

The Christ-child lay on Mary's heart,
His hair was like a fire.
(O weary, weary is the world,
But here the world's desire.)

The Christ-child stood on Mary's knee,
His hair was like a crown,
And all the flowers looked up at Him,
And all the stars looked down.

Letter from the Western Front, Christmas Day 1914

from a British soldier

My Dear sister Janet,

It is 2.00 in the morning and most of our men are asleep in their dugouts – yet I could not sleep myself before writing to you of the wonderful events of Christmas Eve. In truth, what happened seems almost like a fairy tale, and if I hadn't been through it myself, I would scarce believe it. Just imagine: While you and the family sang carols before the fire there in London, I did the same with enemy soldiers here on the battlefields of France!

As I wrote before, there has been little serious fighting of late. The first battles of the war left so many dead that both sides have held back until replacements could come from home. So we have mostly stayed in our trenches and waited.

But what a terrible waiting it has been! Knowing that at any moment an artillery shell might land and explode beside us in the trench, killing or maiming several men. And in daylight not daring to lift our heads above ground, for fear of a sniper's bullet. And the rain – it has fallen almost daily.

Of course, it collects right in our trenches, where we must bail it out with pots and pans. And with the rain has come mud – a good foot or more deep. It splatters and cakes everything, and constantly sucks at our boots. One new recruit got his feet stuck in it and then his hands too when he tried to get out – just like in that American story of the tar baby!

Through all this we couldn't help feel curious about the German soldiers across the way. After all they faced the same dangers we did, and slogged about in the same muck. What's more, their first trench was only 50 yards from ours. Between us lay No Man's Land, bordered on both sides by barbed wire – yet they were close enough we sometimes heard their voices. Of course, we hated them when they killed our friends. But other times we joked about them and almost felt we had something in common. And now it seems they felt the same.

Just yesterday morning – Christmas Eve – we had our first good freeze. Cold as we were we welcomed it, because at least the mud froze solid. Everything was tinged white with frost, while a bright sun shone over all. Perfect Christmas weather. During the day, there was little shelling or rifle fire from either side and as darkness fell on our Christmas Eve, the shooting stopped entirely. Our first complete silence in months! We'd been told the Germans might try and attack and catch us off guard.

I went to the dugout to rest and lying on my cot, I must have drifted asleep. All at once my friend John was shaking me awake, saying 'Come and see! See what the Germans are doing!' I grabbed my rifle, stumbled out into the trench and stuck my head cautiously above the sandbags. I never hope to see a stranger and more lovely sight. Clusters of tiny lights were shining all along the German line, left and right as far as the eye could see 'What is it?' I asked in bewilderment and John answered, 'Christmas trees!'

And so it was. The Germans had placed Christmas trees in front of their trenches, lit by candle or lantern like beacons of goodwill. And then we heard voices raised in song.

Stille nacht, heilige nacht . . .

This carol may not yet be familiar to us in Britain, but John knew it and translated: 'Silent night, holy night.' I've never heard one lovelier – or more meaningful, in that quiet, clear night, its dark softened by a first-quartered moon.

When the song finished, the men in our trenches applauded. Yes British soldiers applauding Germans! Then one of our own men started singing and we all joined in.

The first Nowell, the angel did say . . .

In truth we sounded not nearly as good as the Germans, with their fine harmonies. But they responded with enthusiastic applause of their own and then began another.

O Tannenbaun, o Tannenbaun . . .

Then we replied.

O come all ye faithful . . .

But this time they joined in singing the same words in Latin,

Adeste fideles . . .

British and German harmonizing across No Man's Land! I would have thought nothing could be more amazing – but what came next was more so.

'English, come over!' we heard one of them shout. 'You no shoot, we no shoot.'

Then in the trenches, we looked at each other in bewilderment. Then one of us shouted jokingly, 'You come over here.'

To our astonishment, we saw two figures rise from the trench, climb over their barbed wire and advance unprotected across No Man's Land. One of them called, send officer to talk. I saw one of our men lift his rifle to the ready and no doubt others did the same – but our captain called out 'Hold your fire!' Then he climbed out and went to meet the Germans half way. We heard them talking and a few minutes later, the captain came back with a German cigar in his mouth!

'We've agreed there will be no shooting before midnight tomorrow,' he announced. 'But sentries are to remain on duty and the rest of you stay alert.'

Across the way we could make out groups of two or three men starting out of trenches and coming towards us. Then some of us were climbing out too and in minutes more there were in No Man's Land, over a hundred soldiers and officers of each side, shaking hands with men we'd been trying to kill just hours earlier!

Before long a bonfire was built and around it we mingled – British khaki and German grey. I must say the Germans were the better dressed, with fresh uniforms for the holiday. Only a couple of our men knew German, but more of the Germans knew English. I asked one of them why that was.

'Because many have worked in England!' he said. 'Before all this, I was a waiter at the Hotel Cecil. Perhaps I waited on your table!'

'Perhaps you did!' I said, laughing. He told me he had a girlfriend in London and that war had interrupted their plans for marriage. I told him, 'Don't worry. We'll have you beat by Easter, then you can come back and marry the girl.' He laughed at that.

Then he asked if I'd send her a postcard he'd give me later, and I promised I would. Another German had been a porter at Victoria Station. He showed me a picture of his family back in Munich. His eldest sister was so lovely, I said I should like to meet her someday. He beamed and said he would like that very much and gave me his family's address. Even those who could not converse could still exchange gifts – our cigarettes for their cigars, our tea for their coffee, our corned beef for their sausage. Badges and buttons from uniforms changed owners and one of our lads walked off with the infamous spiked helmet! I myself traded a jack-knife for a leather equipment belt – a fine souvenir to show when I get home.

Newspapers too changed hands and the Germans howled with laughter at ours. They assured us that France was finished and Russia nearly beaten too. We told them that was nonsense and one of them said, 'Well you believe your newspapers and we'll believe ours.' Clearly, they are lied to – yet after meeting these men, I wonder how truthful our newspapers have been. These are not the savage barbarians we've read so much about. They are men with homes and families, hopes and fears, principles and yes love of country. In other words, men like ourselves. Why are we led to believe otherwise?

As it grew late, a few more songs were traded around the fire and then all joined in for – I'm not lying to you – 'Auld Lang Syne'. Then we parted with promises to meet again tomorrow and even some talk of a football match. I was just starting back to the trenched when an older German clutched my arm, 'My God', he said 'why cannot we have peace and go home?' I told him gently,

'That you must ask your Emperor.' He looked at me them, searchingly, 'Perhaps, my friend. But also we must ask our hearts.'

And so dear sister, tell me, has there ever been such a Christmas Eve in all history? And what does it all mean, this impossible befriending of enemies? For the fighting here, of course, it means regrettably little. Decent fellows those soldiers may be, but they follow orders and we do the same. Besides, we are here to stop their army and send it home and never could we shirk that duty.

Still, one cannot help imagine what would happen if the spirit shown here were caught by the nations of the world. Of course, disputes must always arise. But what if our leaders were to offer well wishes in place of warnings? Songs in place of slurs? Presents in place of reprisals? Would not all war end at once? All nations say they want peace. Yet on this Christmas morning, I wonder if we want it quite enough.

Your loving brother,
Tom

The Holly on the Wall

W. H. Davies

Play, little children, one and all,
For holly, holly on the wall.
You do not know that millions are
This moment in a deadly war;
Millions of men whose Christmas bells
Are guns' reports and bursting shells;

Whose holly berries, made of lead,
Take human blood to stain them red;
Whose leaves are swords, and bayonets too,
To pierce their fellow-mortals through.
For now the war is here, and men –
Like cats that stretch their bodies when
The light has gone and darkness comes –
Have armed and left their peaceful homes:
But men will be, when there's no war,
As gentle as you children are.
Play, little children, one and all,
For holly, holly on the wall.

Christmas on the Terra Nova

Robert Falcon Scott

The Terra Nova Expedition, officially the British Antarctic Expedition, was an expedition to Antarctica led by Robert Falcon Scott which took place between 1910 and 1913. On 10 December Terra Nova *met the southern pack ice. It was halted for 20 days before it was able to break clear. Scott attributed the delay to 'sheer bad luck'. This is from his journal for Christmas 1910.*

Friday, December 23. – [. . .] Preparations are now being made for Christmas festivities. It is curious to think that we have already passed the longest day in the southern year. Saw a whale this morning – estimated 25 to 30 feet. Wilson thinks a new species. Find Adélie penguins in batches of twenty or so. Do not remember having seen so many together in the pack.

After midnight, December 23. – Steam was reported ready at

11 p.m. After some pushing to and fro we wriggled out of our ice prison and followed a lead to opener waters [. . .] On the whole in calm water and with a favouring wind we make good progress [. . .]

Saturday, December 24, Christmas Eve. – Alas! alas! at 7 a.m. this morning we were brought up with a solid sheet of pack extending in all directions, save that from which we had come. I must honestly own that I turned in at three thinking we had come to the end of our troubles; I had a suspicion of anxiety when I thought of the size of the floes, but I didn't for a moment suspect we should get into thick pack again behind those great sheets of open water [. . .]

Sunday, December 25, Christmas Day. – The night before last I had bright hopes that this Christmas Day would see us in open water. The scene is altogether too Christmassy. Ice surrounds us, low nimbus clouds intermittently discharging light snow flakes obscure the sky, here and there small pools of open water throw shafts of black shadow on to the cloud – this black predominates in the direction from whence we have come, elsewhere the white haze of ice blink is pervading.

We are captured. We do practically nothing under sail to push through, and could do little under steam, and at each step forward the possibility of advance seems to lessen.

The wind which has persisted from the west for so long fell light last night, and today comes from the N.E. by N., a steady breeze from 2 to 3 in force. Since one must have hope, ours is pinned to the possible effect of a continuance of easterly wind. Again the call is for patience and again patience. Here at least we seem to enjoy full security. The ice is so thin that it could not hurt by pressure – there are no bergs within reasonable distance – indeed the thinness of the ice is one of the most tantalising conditions. In spite of the unpropitious prospect everyone on board is cheerful and one foresees a merry dinner tonight.

The mess is gaily decorated with our various banners. There was full attendance at the Service this morning and a lusty singing of hymns.

Should we now try to go east or west?

I have been trying to go west because the majority of tracks lie that side and no one has encountered such hard conditions as ours – otherwise there is nothing to point to this direction, and all through the last week the prospect to the west has seemed less promising than in other directions; in spite of orders to steer to the S.W. when possible it has been impossible to push in that direction.

An event of Christmas was the production of a family by Crean's rabbit. She gave birth to 17, it is said, and Crean has given away 22!

I don't know what will become of the parent or family; at present they are warm and snug enough, tucked away in the fodder under the forecastle.

Midnight. – Tonight the air is thick with falling snow; the temperature 28°. It is cold and slushy without.

A merry evening has just concluded. We had an excellent dinner: tomato soup, penguin breast stewed as an entrée, roast beef, plum pudding, and mince pies, asparagus, champagne, port and liqueurs – a festive menu. Dinner began at 6 and ended at 7. For five hours the company has been sitting round the table singing lustily; we haven't much talent, but everyone has contributed more or less, and the choruses are deafening. It is rather a surprising circumstance that such an unmusical party should be so keen on singing. On Xmas night it was kept up till 1 a.m., and no work is done without a chanty. I don't know if you have ever heard sea chanties being sung. The merchant sailors have quite a repertoire, and invariably call on it when getting up anchor or hoisting sails. Often as not they are sung in a flat and throaty style, but the effect when a number of men break into the chorus is generally inspiriting.

Christmas at ValleNar Roads
Thomas Benjamin Dixon

Thomas Benjamin Dixon was a young naval surgeon who in later life rose to the rank of Surgeon Captain and was appointed honorary physician to the King. His diary of life at sea details the first year of WW1, and includes an eyewitness account of the Battle of the Falklands, in which Dixon's ship HMS Kent *chased and then sank the Nurnberg after a running battle. Here he describes Christmas 1914 in Chile.*

Christmas Day. Yesterday after coaling some of us tried to get ashore to get holly for decorations. A squall was blowing and although the officers double-banked the oars with the crew of the lifeboat we could make no headway against the wind and tide and ignominiously drifted to leeward. We were seen and rescued by the Glasgow's steam boat which towed us back. Later on in the afternoon the CPOs got there in calmer weather and brought back a boat load of arbutus, laurel, berberis, wild fuchsia trees and plenty of flowers, lilies, fuchsias and unknowns. So this morning we had a fuchsia tree at the top of each mast. Its red flowers made it look just like holly. The crew borrowed some of the officers' clothing and made up to represent us. They held a mock court martial which was great fun and imitated us beautifully. At 12 the Captain visited all the messes followed by the officers who had to taste the various plum puddings and other goodies. It was amazing to see what there was still in the ship in the way of extra food and how cheerful the men were in spite of no beer. In the ward room we had asked the warrant officers and the midshipmen to join us in some champagne before lunch. While there, a parcel arrived from the Mayor of Margate for Dunn. It contained a set of infant's underclothing – Dunn being a bachelor. We hang the articles along the light rail above the table and they made an interesting decoration. The clothes arrived amongst the other things sent by the ladies of Kent apparently. After lunch the crew seized on every officer and carried him round the decks behind the funny party and a 'band'. Some officers went ashore in the afternoon. The PMO being ill in bed with dysentery I stayed aboard. Very hard luck on Fleet Surgeon being ill at such a time. We did our best to cheer him up, however. After the return of the shore party laden with huge tree ferns, fuchsias, etc., we had a sing-song and some excellent new songs, one of which had escaped the lynx-eyed censor (the parson) and was much enjoyed, or at least two verses of it, 'Little by little, and bit by bit.' Our dinner in the evening was a triumph for the Paymaster and the Cook. The decorations of ferns, fuchsias and lilies and baby's garments were really beautiful. Turtle soup. Pate de foie gras, turkey and salmon cutlets, and plenty of fizz and plum pudding. Afterwards the fun was kept up well. Jones' song, and Burn's dancing being the features, especially the latter's last effort in an impromptu Salome costume. The Captain was our guest for the evening. We all remarked that it was the cheeriest Christmas on a ship we could remember and felt sorry for the sad folk (probably) at home.

Letter to her brother

Caroline Darwin

My dear Charles,
Christmas day 25th, 1831

We have all been thinking of you & wishing you a happy Xmas, which to be sure is rather a farce knowing as we all do that you are pitching & tossing & as sick as may be – I was never more astonished when sitting painting quietly & believing you to be half way to the Madeiras to receive your two letters from Devonport & such long, interesting, agreeable letters. I am exceedingly glad you feel so much at home & comfortably established in the Beagle & if you are reconciled now to the confinement, so soon after going on board – I think with your Captain, & that you must fully deserve his compliment of being the best of shore going fellows [. . .]

I have read & re read so many times your letters that I know them by heart, almost I should say for you & I agree our memory is not our strongest point – I have just seen my Father he sends you his kindest love. I wish you had seen his pleased feeling look when I read him yr affection-ate message.

Good bye my very very dear Charles

Yrs very affectly

Caroline Darwin

A Slice of Plum Pudding

from *Father and Son*, Edmund Gosse

My Father's austerity of behaviour was, I think, perpetually accentuated by his fear of doing anything to offend the consciences of these persons, whom he supposed, no doubt, to be more sensitive than they really were. He was fond of saying that 'a very little stain upon the conscience makes a wide breach in our communion with God', and he counted possible errors of conduct by hundreds and by thousands. It was in this winter that his attention was particularly drawn to the festival of Christmas, which, apparently, he had scarcely noticed in London.

On the subject of all feasts of the Church he held views of an almost grotesque peculiarity. He looked upon each of them as nugatory and worthless, but the keeping of Christmas appeared to him by far the most hateful, and nothing less than an act of idolatry. 'The very word is Popish,' he used to exclaim, 'Christ's Mass!' pursing up his lips with the gesture of one who tastes assafoetida by accident. Then he would adduce the antiquity of the so-called feast, adapted from horrible heathen rites, and itself a soiled relic of the abominable Yule-Tide. He would denounce the horrors of Christmas until it almost made me blush to look at a holly berry.

On Christmas Day of this year 1857 our villa saw a very unusual sight. My Father had given strictest charge that no difference whatever was to be made in our meals on that day; the dinner was to be neither more copious than usual nor less so. He was obeyed, but the servants, secretly rebellious, made a small plum pudding for themselves. (I discovered afterwards, with pain, that Miss Marks received a slice of it in her boudoir.) Early in the afternoon, the maids – of whom we were now advanced to keeping two – kindly remarked that 'the poor dear child ought to have a bit, anyhow', and wheedled me into the kitchen, where I ate a slice of plum pudding. Shortly I began to feel that pain inside which in my frail state was inevitable, and my conscience smote me violently. At length I could bear my spiritual anguish no longer, and bursting into the study I called out: 'Oh! Papa, Papa, I have eaten of flesh offered to idols!' It took some time, between my sobs, to explain what had happened. Then my Father sternly said: 'Where is the accursed thing?' I explained that as much as was left of it was still on the kitchen table. He took me by the hand, and ran with me into the midst of the startled servants, seized what remained of the pudding, and with the plate in one hand and me still tight in the other, ran till we reached the dust-heap, when he flung the idolatrous confectionery on to the middle of the ashes, and then raked it deep down into the mass. The suddenness, the violence, the velocity of this extraordinary act made an impression on my memory which nothing will ever efface.

Xmas Day in the Desert

Gunner Dick Haydon

The Siege of Tobruk, Libya lasted for 241 days in 1941. While serving with 153 Heavy Anti-Aircraft Battery, which had played a big part In the successful defence of Tobruk, Gunner Dick Haydon composed a poem.

> Twas Xmas day in the desert,
> The place was bleak and drear,
> And all the Gunners' faces
> Were not aglow with beer.
> For 12 months in the desert
> Amidst the toil and strife,
> Without their beer and comforts
> Had soured each sweet life.
>
> And now, at last, 'twas Xmas
> That day of Xmas pud,
> When each man should be sozzled,
> And more so if he could.

Alas for that great dinner,
Instead of grub so nice,
The Gunners only saw a pile
Of bully beef and rice.

And then in 'crowning' glory
The Major did appear,
To tell the boys of their good work
And curse the lack of beer.

You've all done damn good work, Boys
And giv'n the Hun a bashin'
So for your Xmas dinner
You'll get a double ration.

This set the men a'talking
And frowning quite a lot,
They'd all worked hard – and this reward
Just hit them like a shot.

Until with one accord they said
In words that were a farce
'Just keep your Xmas dinner, Sir,
And stick it up your vase!'

Christmas Dinner at the Cratchits'

from *A Christmas Carol*, Charles Dickens

Such a bustle ensued that you might have thought a goose the
rarest of all birds; a feathered phenomenon, to which a black

swan was a matter of course – and in truth it was something very like it in that house. Mrs Cratchit made the gravy (ready beforehand in a little saucepan) hissing hot; Master Peter mashed the potatoes with incredible vigour; Miss Belinda sweetened up the apple sauce; Martha dusted the hot plates; Bob took Tiny Tim beside him in a tiny corner at the table; the two young Cratchits set chairs for everybody, not forgetting themselves, and mounting guard upon their posts, crammed spoons into their mouths, lest they should shriek for goose before their turn came to be helped. At last the dishes were set on, and grace was said. It was succeeded by a breathless pause, as Mrs Cratchit, looking slowly all along the carving-knife, prepared to plunge it in the breast; but when she did, and when the long expected gush of stuffing issued forth, one murmur of delight arose all round the board, and even Tiny Tim, excited by the two young Cratchits, beat on the table with the handle of his knife, and feebly cried 'Hurrah!'

There never was such a goose. Bob said he didn't believe there ever was such a goose cooked. Its tenderness and flavour, size and cheapness, were the themes of universal admiration. Eked out by apple sauce and mashed potatoes, it was a sufficient dinner for the whole family; indeed, as Mrs Cratchit said with great delight (surveying one small atom of a bone upon the dish), they hadn't ate it all at last! Yet every one had had enough, and the youngest Cratchits in particular, were steeped in sage and onion to the eyebrows! But now, the plates being changed by Miss Belinda, Mrs Cratchit left the room alone – too nervous to bear witnesses – to take the pudding up and bring it in.

Suppose it should not be done enough! Suppose it should break in turning out! Suppose somebody should have got over the wall of the backyard, and stolen it, while they were merry with the goose – a supposition at which the two young Cratchits became livid! All sorts of horrors were supposed.

Hallo! A great deal of steam! The pudding was out of the copper. A smell like a washing-day! That was the cloth. A smell like an eating-house and a pastrycook's next door to each other, with a laundress's next door to that! That was the pudding! In half a minute Mrs Cratchit entered – flushed, but smiling proudly – with the pudding, like a speckled cannon-ball, so hard and firm, blazing in half of half-a-quartern of ignited brandy, and bedight with Christmas holly stuck into the top.

Oh, a wonderful pudding! Bob Cratchit said, and calmly too, that he regarded it as the greatest success achieved by Mrs Cratchit since their marriage. Mrs Cratchit said that now the weight was off her mind, she would confess she had had her doubts about the quantity of flour. Everybody had something to say about it, but nobody said or thought it was at all a small pudding for a large family. It would have been flat heresy to do so. Any Cratchit would have blushed to hint at such a thing.

At last the dinner was all done, the cloth was cleared, the hearth swept, and the fire made up. The compound in the jug being tasted, and considered perfect, apples and oranges were put upon the table, and a shovel-full of chestnuts on the fire. Then all the Cratchit family drew round the hearth, in what Bob Cratchit called a circle, meaning half a one; and at Bob Cratchit's elbow stood the family display of glass. Two tumblers, and a custard-cup without a handle.

These held the hot stuff from the jug, however, as well as golden goblets would have done; and Bob served it out with beaming looks, while the chestnuts on the fire sputtered and cracked noisily.

Then Bob proposed: 'A Merry Christmas to us all, my dears. God bless us!'

Which all the family re-echoed.

'God bless us every one!' said Tiny Tim, the last of all.

Christmas at Chatsworth

Harold Macmillan

The ritual did not differ from year to year. All assembled the day before. As each family arrived, 'Granny Evie' received them at the top of the stairs where the Outer Hall led into the passage leading to the great Painted Hall. My children still remember her greeting each family in turn – always in her place, as the cars passed the lodge – a gracious and dignified figure, dressed in dark colours and long flowing dresses, never changing. Shy and reserved as she was, with the children, like the Duke, she had no inhibitions. The sons-in-law, of course, soon learnt the desirability of sending their families by the early train, and ensuring sufficient important business in London to make it necessary for them to follow later and more comfortably.

Christmas Eve in this, as in every other home throughout the land, was a flurry of mothers filling and hanging stockings, decorating nurseries, and getting to bed very late themselves. All this is still carried on in a modified form in my own home as, happily, in many other houses. Children and grandchildren gather yearly for the great festival.

Christmas Day. Early to church at eight o'clock across the park in the darkness; then breakfast and the morning with the enjoyment of minor presents. Balloons to be inflated, trumpets to be blown, and roller-skates to be tried out. No house is better fitted for roller-skating. The whole course is good, with particularly fast going on the stone floor of the Statue Gallery and the Orangery. Then Matins at the parish church in the park, with a full and overflowing congregation; all the familiar hymns; and a mercifully short sermon. The clergyman likes to be asked to shoot, and the Duke, though he says little, has a good memory.

Christmas lunch, to which children over a certain age were allowed – the rules strictly enforced – and then the photograph. In those days the ingenious methods by which these can be taken indoors had not been invented. We all trooped out to a particularly cold and draughty part of the garden – by Flora's Temple, outside the Orangery. When at last all the generations could be brought into some kind of order, the yearly photograph was taken. Each year showed a steady increase and, happily, no casualties – not yet. A walk in the garden followed, which was supposed to be healthy and after the Christmas cheer was no doubt salutary.

One of the old traditions of Chatsworth scrupulously maintained was Evensong every Sunday in the house chapel. Those who know Chatsworth will remember the great beauty of this masterpiece of late seventeenth-century work, with its lovely altar and the fine ceiling. The village organist and choir came up for the service. Two rows of straight Jacobean chairs stood facing each other. On one side were the men; on the other the women. When the house was full, with all the guests, servants, and visiting servants, there was a goodly company. The service always ended with the same hymn, called the Benediction hymn, sung kneeling:

> Father give us now Thy Blessing,
>   Take us now beneath Thy Care;
> May we all enjoy Thy presence.
>   And Thy tender mercies share.
>
> Guard us through this night from danger,
>   Keep us in Thy heavenly love;
> Through our life do Thou be near us,
>   Then receive us all above.

Its origin is unknown.

The weather at Chatsworth was of two kinds and both in an extreme form. Sometimes the glass was low and the temperature mild. Then it was dark, rainy, foggy, and uninviting. Or there could be a high glass, with snow and ice and tobogganing and skating. These were the Christmases I remember with the keenest pleasure – the beauty of the great trees in the garden and park, and the house shining with a strangely golden glow in the rays of the low winter sun. The weather played an important part in the daily routine. Following a custom of many generations, every day at breakfast there was placed on one of the splendid Kent side-tables a book recording the temperature, the hours of sunshine, and the rainfall, compiled by one of the gardeners. The Duke studied this every morning, carefully, but without emotion.

After tea on Christmas Day came the ceremony of presents given and received. This took place in the Statue Gallery, where stood the huge tree. First, all the presents to the servants, taken round by the children; then presents from children to grown-ups; then, at last, the children's own presents from all their different relations. They were perhaps not so expensive or so elaborate as they are today, but with the enormous family interchange, they were very numerous.

Boxing Day. Children who survived (there were always some casualties to colds or over-excitement) went off to the meet of the High Peak Harriers at Bakewell. At this time my sister-in-law Maud Baillie and her husband Evan were the Joint Masters. It was a great gathering of local sportsmen, including many children, coming from far and wide. There was no shooting on Boxing Day so that all the men on the place could enjoy their holiday. For those who did not hunt it was, therefore, a day of sleep, or bridge, or reading. During the next few days there was shooting – and good shooting – and then some of the older members of the party began to disperse. But the mothers and children generally stayed on for two or three weeks, the fathers returning each weekend for more shooting. At last, reluctantly, but with a sense of great achievement, this large family party came to an end until the next year.

King John's Christmas

A. A. Milne

King John was not a good man –
He had his little ways.
And sometimes no one spoke to him
For days and days and days.
And men who came across him,
When walking in the town,
Gave him a supercilious stare,
Or passed with noses in the air –
And bad King John stood dumbly there,
Blushing beneath his crown.

King John was not a good man,
And no good friends had he.
He stayed in every afternoon . . .
But no one came to tea.
And, round about December,
The cards upon his shelf
Which wished him lots of Christmas cheer,
And fortune in the coming year,
Were never from his near and dear,
But only from himself.

King John was not a good man,
Yet had his hopes and fears.
They'd given him no present now
For years and years and years.
But every year at Christmas,
While minstrels stood about,
Collecting tribute from the young
For all the songs they might have sung,
He stole away upstairs and hung
A hopeful stocking out.

King John was not a good man,
He lived his life aloof;
Alone he thought a message out
While climbing up the roof.
He wrote it down and propped it
Against the chimney stack:
'TO ALL AND SUNDRY – NEAR AND FAR –
F. CHRISTMAS IN PARTICULAR.'
And signed it not 'Johannes R.'
But very humbly, 'Jack.'

'I want some crackers,
And I want some candy;
I think a box of chocolates
Would come in handy;
I don't mind oranges,
I do like nuts!
And I SHOULD like a pocket-knife
That really cuts.
And, oh! Father Christmas, if you love me at all,
Bring me a big, red, india-rubber ball!'

King John was not a good man –
He wrote this message out,
And gat him to this room again,
Descending by the spout.
And all that night he lay there,
A prey to hopes and fears.
'I think that's him a-coming now!'
(Anxiety bedewed his brow.)
'He'll bring one present, anyhow –
The first I had for years.'

'Forget about the crackers,
And forget the candy;
I'm sure a box of chocolates
Would never come in handy;
I don't like oranges,
I don't want nuts,
And I HAVE got a pocket-knife
That almost cuts.
But, oh! Father Christmas, if you love me at all,
Bring me a big, red, india-rubber ball!'

King John was not a good man,
Next morning when the sun
Rose up to tell a waiting world
That Christmas had begun,
And people seized their stockings,
And opened them with glee,
And crackers, toys and games appeared,
And lips with sticky sweets were smeared,
King John said grimly: 'As I feared,
Nothing again for me!'

'I did want crackers,
And I did want candy;
I know a box of chocolates
Would come in handy;
I do love oranges,
I did want nuts!
And, oh! if Father Christmas, had loved me at all,
He would have brought a big, red,
india–rubber ball!'

King John stood by the window,
And frowned to see below
The happy bands of boys and girls
All playing in the snow.
A while he stood there watching,
And envying them all . . .
When through the window big and red
There hurtled by his royal head,
And bounced and fell upon the bed,
An india–rubber ball!

AND, OH, FATHER CHRISTMAS,
MY BLESSINGS ON YOU FALL
FOR BRINGING HIM
A BIG, RED,
INDIA–RUBBER
BALL!

Diary, Christmas Day 1955
Noel Coward

Beverly Hills

In the middle of it all again. This house is really very nice and I have a dusky Jamaican lady to look after me who is lackadaisical and hums constantly. There have been a series of parties as usual, each one indistinguishable from the other, culminating last night in the [Humphrey] Bogarts' Christmas Eve revel which was great fun and highly glamorous to the eye. The Christmas shopping has been frantic as usual. Clifton [Webb] is sweet but inclined to bouts of slightly bibulous self-pity on account of being lonely. Mabelle [Clifton's mother] is indestructible and gets on his nerves, also he has no picture settled, so he is idle. We had a successful reading of the play at the Bogarts' last Sunday and everyone read well. Betty [Lauren] Bacall will be good, I think, and anyhow she is word perfect which is wonderful considering she was shooting a picture until yesterday.

I have acquired some nice Christmas loot. Exquisite gold and ebony monogrammed links from Frank Sinatra, and a lovely black dressing-gown and pyjamas to match from Marlene [Dietrich], and hand-worked bedroom slippers from Merle [Oberon] which are charming. A lot of other nice gifts too, but oh I *do* wish Christmas hadn't coincided with *Blithe Spirit*. There is so much to be done and, it seems, so little time to do it.

The Christmas Dinner
Washington Irving

After the dinner-table was removed, the hall was given up to the younger members of the family, who, prompted to all kind of noisy mirth by the Oxonian and Master Simon, made its old walls ring with their merriment, as they played at romping games. I delight in witnessing the gambols of children, and particularly at this happy holiday-season, and could not help stealing out of the drawing room on hearing one of their peals of laughter. I found them at the game of blindman's buff. Master Simon, who was the leader of their revels, and seemed on all occasions to fulfil the office of that ancient potentate, the Lord of Misrule, was blinded in the midst of the hall. The little beings were as busy about him as the mock fairies about Falstaff; pinching him, plucking at the skirts of his coat, and tickling him with straws. One fine blue-eyed girl of about thirteen, with her flaxen hair all in beautiful confusion, her frolic face in a glow, her frock half torn off her shoulders, a complete picture of a romp, was the chief tormentor; and from the slyness with which Master Simon avoided the smaller game, and hemmed this wild little nymph in corners, and obliged her to jump shrieking over chairs, I suspected the rogue of being not a whit more blinded than was convenient.

When I returned to the drawing room, I found the company seated round the fire, listening to the parson, who was deeply ensconced in a high-backed oaken chair, the work of some cunning artificer of yore, which had been brought from the library for his particular accommodation. From this venerable piece of furniture, with which his shadowy figure and dark weazen face so admirably accorded, he was dealing forth strange accounts of the popular superstitions and legends of the surrounding country, with which he had become acquainted in the course of his antiquarian researches. I am half inclined to think that the old gentleman was himself somewhat tinctured with superstition, as men are very apt to be who live a recluse and studious life in a sequestered part of the country, and pore over black-letter tracts, so often filled with the marvellous and supernatural. He gave us several anecdotes of the fancies of the neighbouring peasantry, concerning the effigy of the crusader which lay on the tomb by the church altar. As it was the only monument of the kind in that part of the country, it had always been regarded with feelings of superstition by the goodwives of the village. It was said to get up from the tomb and walk the rounds of the churchyard in stormy nights, particularly when it thundered; and one old woman, whose cottage bordered on the churchyard, had seen it, through the windows of the church, when the moon shone, slowly pacing up and down the aisles. It was the belief that some wrong had been left unredressed by the deceased, or some treasure hidden, which kept the spirit in a state of trouble and restlessness. Some talked of gold and jewels buried in the tomb, over which the spectre kept watch; and there was a story current of a sexton in old times who endeavoured to break his way to the coffin at night; but just as he reached it, received a violent blow from the marble hand of the effigy, which stretched him senseless on the pavement. These tales were often laughed at by some of the sturdier among the rustics, yet when night came on, there were many of the stoutest unbelievers that were shy of venturing alone in the footpath that led across the churchyard.

From these and other anecdotes that followed, the crusader appeared to be the favourite hero of ghost stories throughout the vicinity. His picture, which hung up in the hall, was thought by the servants to have something supernatural about it; for they remarked that, in whatever part of the hall you went, the eyes of the warrior were still fixed on you. The old porter's wife, too, at the lodge, who had been born and brought up in the family, and was a great gossip among the maid-servants, affirmed, that in her young days she had often heard say, that on Midsummer eve, when it is well known all kinds of ghosts, goblins, and fairies become visible and walk abroad, the crusader used to mount his horse, come down from his picture, ride about the house, down the avenue, and so to the church to visit the tomb: on which occasion the church door most civilly swung open of itself: not that he needed it: for he rode through closed gates and even stone walls, and had been seen by one of the dairymaids to pass between two bars of the great park gate, making himself as thin as a sheet of paper.

All these superstitions I found had been very much countenanced by the Squire, who, though not superstitious himself, was very fond of seeing others so. He listened to every goblin tale of the neighbouring gossips with infinite gravity, and held the porter's wife in high favour on account of her talent for the marvellous. He was himself a great reader of old legends and romances, and often lamented that he could not believe in them; for a superstitious person, he thought, must live in a kind of fairyland.

Whilst we were all attention to the parson's stories, our ears were suddenly assailed by a burst of heterogeneous sounds from the hall, in which was mingled something like the clang of rude minstrelsy, with the uproar of many small voices and girlish laughter. The door suddenly flew open, and a train came trooping into the room, that might almost have been mistaken for the breaking up of the court of Fairy. That indefatigable spirit, Master Simon, in the faithful discharge of his duties as Lord of Misrule, had conceived the idea of a Christmas mummery, or masking; and having called in to his assistance the Oxonian and the young officer, who were equally ripe for anything that should occasion romping and merriment, they had carried it into instant effect. The old housekeeper had been consulted; the antique clothes-presses and wardrobes rummaged and made to yield up the relics of finery that had not seen the light for several generations; the younger part of the company had been privately convened from the parlour and hall, and the whole had been bedizened out, into a burlesque imitation of an antique masque.

Master Simon led the van, as 'Ancient Christmas', quaintly apparelled in a ruff, a short cloak, which had very much the aspect of one of the old housekeeper's petticoats, and a hat that might have served for a village steeple, and must indubitably have figured in the days of the Covenanters. From under this his nose curved boldly forth, flushed with a frost-bitten bloom, that seemed the very trophy of a December blast. He was accompanied by the blue-eyed romp, dished up as 'Dame Mince Pie', in the venerable magnificence of faded brocade, long stomacher, peaked hat, and high-heeled shoes. The young officer appeared as Robin Hood, in a sporting dress of Kendal green, and a foraging cap with a gold tassel. The costume, to be sure, did not bear testimony to deep research, and there was an evident eye to the picturesque, natural to a young gallant in the presence of his mistress. The fair Julia hung on his arm in a pretty rustic dress, as 'Maid Marian'. The rest of the train had been metamorphosed in various ways; the girls trussed up in the finery of the ancient belles of the Bracebridge line, and the striplings bewhiskered with burnt cork, and gravely clad in broad skirts, hanging sleeves, and full-bottomed wigs, to represent the characters of Roast Beef, Plum Pudding and other worthies celebrated in ancient maskings. The whole was under the control of the Oxonian, in the appropriate character of Misrule; and I observed that he exercised rather a mischievous sway with his wand over the smaller personages of the pageant.

The irruption of this motley crew, with beat of drum, according to ancient custom, was the consummation of uproar and merriment. Master Simon covered himself with glory by the stateliness with which, as Ancient Christmas, he walked a minuet with the peerless, though giggling, Dame Mince Pie. It was followed by a dance of all the characters, which, from its medley of costumes, seemed as though the old family portraits had skipped down from their frames to join in the sport. Different centuries were figuring at cross hands and right and left; the dark ages were cutting pirouettes and rigadoons; and the days of Queen Bess jigging merrily down the middle, through a line of succeeding generations.

The worthy Squire contemplated these fantastic sports, and this resurrection of his old wardrobe, with the simple relish of childish delight. He stood chuckling and rubbing his hands, and scarcely hearing a word the parson said, notwithstanding that the latter was discoursing most authentically on the ancient and stately dance at the Paon, or Peacock, from which he conceived the minuet to be derived. For my part, I was in a continual excitement, from the varied scenes of whim and innocent gaiety passing before me. It was inspiring to see wild-eyed frolic and warm-hearted hospitality breaking out from among the chills and glooms of winter, and old age throwing off his apathy, and catching once more the freshness of youthful enjoyment. I felt also an interest in the scene, from the consideration that these fleeting customs were posting fast into oblivion, and that this was, perhaps, the only family in England in which the whole of them were still punctiliously observed. There was a quaintness, too, mingled with all this revelry that gave it a peculiar zest; it was suited to the time and place; and as the old Manor House almost reeled with mirth and wassail, it seemed echoing back the joviality of long-departed years.

But enough of Christmas and its gambols; it is time for me to pause in this garrulity. Methinks I hear the questions asked by my graver readers, 'To what purpose is all this? – how is the world to be made wiser by this talk?' Alas! Is there not wisdom enough extant for the instruction of the world? And if not, are there not thousands of abler pens labouring for its improvement? – It is so much pleasanter to please than to instruct – to play the companion rather than the preceptor.

What, after all, is the mite of wisdom that I could throw into the mass of knowledge? Or how am I sure that my sagest deductions may be safe guides for the opinions of others? But in writing to amuse, if I fail, the only evil is my own disappointment. If, however, I can by any lucky chance, in these days of evil, rub out one wrinkle from the brow of care, or beguile the heavy heart of one moment of sorrow; if I can now and then penetrate through the gathering film of misanthropy, prompt a benevolent view of human nature, and make my reader more in good humour with his fellow beings and himself, surely, surely, I shall not then have written entirely in vain.

The Christmas Pudding is a Mediterranean Food
Elizabeth David

Now, all those with their fine talk of the glories of Old English fare, have they ever actually made Christmas pudding, in large quantities, by Old English methods? Have they for instance ever tried cleaning and skinning, flouring, shredding, chopping beef kidney suet straight off the hoof? Have they ever stoned bunch after bunch of raisins hardly yet dry on the stalk and each one as sticky as a piece of warm toffee? And how long do they think it takes to bash up three pounds of breadcrumbs without an oven in which they could first dry the loaves? Come to that, what would they make of an attempt to boil, and to keep on the boil for nine to ten hours on two charcoal fires let into holes in the wall, some dozen large puddings? Well, I had nothing much else to do in those days and quite enjoyed all the work, but I'd certainly never let myself in for such an undertaking again. Nor, indeed, would I again attempt to explain the principles of a hay box and the reasons for making one to peasants of whose language I had such a scanty knowledge and who are in any case notoriously unreceptive to the idea of having hot food, or for that matter hot water or hot coffee, hotter than tepid.

All things considered, my puddings turned out quite nicely. The ones which emerged from the hay box were at just about the right temperature – lukewarm. They were sweet and dark and rich. My village friends were not as enthusiastic as they had been about the mustard pickles. What with so many of the company having participated in the construction of the hay box, my assurances that the raisins and the currants grown and dried there on the spot in the Greek sun were richer and more juicy than the artificially dried, hygienically treated and much-travelled variety we got at home, my observations on the incomparable island-made candied citron and orange peel (that was fun to cut up too) given me by the neighbours, and the memorable scent of violets and brilliantine given to the puddings by Athenian brandy, a certain amount of the English mystery had disappeared from our great national festive dish.

That *le plum pudding n'est pas Anglais* was a startling discovery made by a French chef, Philéas Gilbert, round about the turn of the century. No, not English indeed. In this case le plum pudding had been almost Greek. What I wish I'd known at the time was the rest of Gilbert's story. It seems that with a passing nod to a Breton concoction called *le far* 'obviously the ancestor of the English pudding', an earlier French historian.

Bourdeau by name, unable or perhaps unwilling to claim plum pudding for France, says that it is precisely described by Athenaeus in a report of the wedding feast of Caranus, an Argive prince, The pudding was called *strepte*, and in origin was entirely Greek.

Under the Mistletoe

from *The Pickwick Papers*, Charles Dickens

From the centre of the ceiling of this kitchen, old Wardle had just suspended, with his own hands, a huge branch of mistletoe, and this same branch of mistletoe instantaneously gave rise to a scene of general and most delightful struggling and confusion; in the midst of which, Mr Pickwick, with a gallantry that would have done honour to a descendant of Lady Tollimglower herself, took the old lady by the hand, led her beneath the mystic branch, and saluted her in all courtesy and decorum. The old lady submitted to this piece of practical politeness with all the dignity which befitted so important and serious a solemnity, but the younger ladies, not being so thoroughly imbued with a superstitious veneration for the custom, or imagining that the value of a salute is very much enhanced if it cost a little trouble to obtain it, screamed and struggled, and ran into corners, and threatened and remonstrated, and did everything but leave the room, until some of the less adventurous gentlemen were on the point of desisting, when they all at once found it useless to resist any longer, and submitted to be kissed with a good grace. Mr Winkle kissed the young lady with the black eyes, and Mr Snodgrass kissed Emily; and Mr Weller, not being particular about the form of being under the mistletoe, kissed Emma and the other female servants, just as he caught them. As to the poor relations, they kissed everybody, not even excepting the plainer portions of the young lady visitors, who, in their excessive confusion, ran right under the mistletoe, as soon as it was hung up, without knowing it! Wardle stood with his back to the fire, surveying the whole scene, with the utmost satisfaction; and the fat boy took the opportunity of appropriating to his own use, and summarily devouring, a particularly fine mince pie, that had been carefully put by, for somebody else.

Now, the screaming had subsided, and faces were in a glow, and curls in a tangle, and Mr Pickwick, after kissing the old lady as before mentioned, was standing under the mistletoe, looking with a very pleased countenance on all that was passing around him, when the young lady with the black eyes, after a little whispering with the other young ladies, made a sudden dart forward, and, putting her arm round Mr Pickwick's neck, saluted him affectionately on the left cheek; and before Mr Pickwick distinctly knew what was the matter, he was surrounded by the whole body, and kissed by every one of them.

It was a pleasant thing to see Mr Pickwick in the centre of the group, now pulled this way, and then that, and first kissed on the chin, and then on the nose, and then on the spectacles, and to hear the peals of laughter which were raised on every side; but it was a still more pleasant thing to see Mr Pickwick, blinded shortly afterwards with a silk handkerchief, falling up against the wall, and scrambling into corners, and going through all the mysteries of blind-man's buff, with the utmost relish for the game, until at last he caught one of the poor relations, and then had to evade the blind-man himself, which he did with a nimbleness and agility that elicited the admiration and applause of all beholders. The poor relations caught the people who they thought would like it, and, when the game flagged, got caught themselves. When they all tired of blind-man's buff, there was a great game at snap-dragon, and when fingers enough were burned with that, and all the raisins were gone, they sat down by the huge fire of blazing logs to a substantial supper, and a mighty bowl of wassail, something smaller than an ordinary wash-house copper, in which the hot apples were hissing and bubbling with a rich look, and a jolly sound, that were perfectly irresistible.

'This,' said Mr Pickwick, looking round him, 'this is, indeed, comfort.'

'Our invariable custom,' replied Mr Wardle. 'Everybody sits down with us on Christmas Eve, as you see them now – servants and all; and here we wait, until the clock strikes twelve, to usher Christmas in, and beguile the time with forfeits and old stories. Trundle, my boy, rake up the fire.'

Up flew the bright sparks in myriads as the logs were stirred. The deep red blaze sent forth a rich glow, that penetrated into the farthest corner of the room, and cast its cheerful tint on every face.

'Come,' said Wardle, 'a song – a Christmas song! I'll give you one, in default of a better.'

'Bravo!' said Mr Pickwick.

'Fill up,' cried Wardle. 'It will be two hours, good, before you see the bottom of the bowl through the deep rich colour of the wassail; fill up all round, and now for the song.'

Thus saying, the merry old gentleman, in a good, round, sturdy voice, commenced without more ado –

A CHRISTMAS CAROL

'I care not for Spring; on his fickle wing
Let the blossoms and buds be borne;
He woos them amain with his treacherous rain,
And he scatters them ere the morn.

An inconstant elf, he knows not himself,
Nor his own changing mind an hour,
He'll smile in your face, and, with wry grimace,
He'll wither your youngest flower.

'Let the Summer sun to his bright home run,
He shall never be sought by me;
When he's dimmed by a cloud I can laugh aloud
And care not how sulky he be!
For his darling child is the madness wild
That sports in fierce fever's train;
And when love is too strong, it don't last long,
As many have found to their pain.

'A mild harvest night, by the tranquil light
Of the modest and gentle moon,
Has a far sweeter sheen for me, I ween,
Than the broad and unblushing noon.
But every leaf awakens my grief,
As it lieth beneath the tree;
So let Autumn air be never so fair,
It by no means agrees with me.

'But my song I troll out, for Christmas Stout,
The hearty, the true, and the bold;
A bumper I drain, and with might and main
Give three cheers for this Christmas old!
We'll usher him in with a merry din
That shall gladden his joyous heart,
And we'll keep him up, while there's bite or sup,
And in fellowship good, we'll part.

'In his fine honest pride, he scorns to hide
One jot of his hard-weather scars;

They're no disgrace, for there's much the same trace
On the cheeks of our bravest tars.
Then again I sing till the roof doth ring
And it echoes from wall to wall –
To the stout old wight, fair welcome tonight,
As the King of the Seasons all.'

Christmas Day, 1843

Lord Shaftesbury

'This is the day that the Lord hath made; let us rejoice and be glad in it.'

Rose before six to prayer and meditation. Ah, blessed God, how many in the mills and factories have risen at four, on this day even, to toil and suffering!

The Shop of Ghosts

G. K. Chesterton

Nearly all the best and most precious things in the universe you can get for a halfpenny. I make an exception, of course, of the sun, the moon, the earth, people, stars, thunderstorms, and such trifles. You can get them for nothing. Also I make an exception of another thing, which I am not allowed to mention in this paper, and of which the lowest price is a penny halfpenny. But the general principle will be at once apparent. In the street behind me, for instance, you can now get a ride on an electric tram for a halfpenny. To be on an electric tram is to be on a flying castle in a fairy tale. You can get quite a large number of brightly coloured sweets for a halfpenny. Also you can get the chance of reading this article for a halfpenny; along, of course, with other and irrelevant matter.

But if you want to see what a vast and bewildering array of valuable things you can get at a halfpenny each you should do as I was doing last night. I was gluing my nose against the glass of a very small and dimly lit toyshop in one of the greyest and leanest of the streets of Battersea. But dim as was that square of light, it was filled (as a child once said to me) with all the colours God ever made. Those toys of the poor were like the children who buy them; they were all dirty; but they were all bright. For my part, I think brightness more important than cleanliness; since the first is of the soul, and the second of the body. You must excuse me; I am a democrat; I know I am out of fashion in the modern world.

As I looked at that palace of pigmy wonders, at small green omnibuses, at small blue elephants, at small black dolls, and small red Noah's arks, I must have fallen into some sort of unnatural trance. That lit shop window became like the brilliantly lit stage when one is watching some highly coloured comedy. I forgot the grey houses and the grimy people behind me as one forgets the dark galleries and the dim crowds at a theatre. It seemed as if the little objects behind the glass were small, not because they were toys, but because they were objects far away. The green omnibus was really a green omnibus, a green Bayswater omnibus, passing across some huge desert on its ordinary way to Bayswater. The blue elephant was no longer blue with paint; he was blue with distance. The black doll was really a negro relieved against passionate tropic foliage in the land where every weed is flaming and only man is black. The red Noah's ark was really the enormous ship of earthly salvation riding on the rain-swollen sea, red in the first morning of hope.

Every one, I suppose, knows such stunning instants of abstraction, such brilliant blanks in the mind. In such moments one can see the face of one's own best friend as an unmeaning pattern of spectacles or moustaches. They are commonly marked by the two signs of the slowness of their growth and the suddenness of their termination. The return to real thinking is often as abrupt as bumping into a man. Very often indeed (in my case) it is bumping into a man. But in any case the awakening is always emphatic and, generally speaking, it is always complete. Now, in this case, I did come back with a shock of sanity to the consciousness that I was, after all, only staring into a dingy little toyshop; but in some strange way the mental cure did not seem to be final. There was still in my mind an unmanageable something that told me that I had strayed into some odd atmosphere, or that I had already done some odd thing. I felt as if I had worked a miracle or committed a sin. It was as if I had at any rate, stepped across some border in the soul.

To shake off this dangerous and dreamy sense I went into the shop and tried to buy wooden soldiers. The man in the shop was very old and broken, with confused white hair covering his head and half his face, hair so startlingly white that it looked almost artificial. Yet though he was senile and even sick, there was nothing of suffering in his eyes; he looked rather as if he were gradually falling asleep in a not unkindly decay. He gave me the wooden soldiers, but when I put down the money he did not at first seem to see it; then he blinked at it feebly, and then he pushed it feebly away.

'No, no,' he said vaguely. 'I never have. I never have. We are rather old-fashioned here.'

'Not taking money,' I replied, 'seems to me more like an uncommonly new fashion than an old one.'

'I never have,' said the old man, blinking and blowing his nose; 'I've always given presents. I'm too old to stop.'

'Good heavens!' I said. 'What can you mean? Why, you might be Father Christmas.'

'I am Father Christmas,' he said apologetically, and blew his nose again.

The lamps could not have been lighted yet in the street outside. At any rate, I could see nothing against the darkness but the shining shop window. There were no sounds of steps or voices in the street; I might have strayed into some new and sunless world. But something had cut the chords of common sense, and I could not feel even surprise except sleepily. Something made me say, 'You look ill, Father Christmas.'

'I am dying,' he said.

I did not speak, and it was he who spoke again.

'All the new people have left my shop. I cannot understand it. They seem to object to me on such curious and inconsistent sort of grounds, these scientific men, and these innovators. They say that I give people superstitions and make them too visionary; they say I give people sausages and make them too coarse. They say my heavenly parts are too heavenly; they say my earthly parts are too earthly; I don't know what they want, I'm sure. How can heavenly things be too heavenly, or earthly things too earthly? How can one be too good, or too jolly? I don't understand. But I understand one thing well enough. These modern people are living and I am dead.'

'You may be dead,' I replied. 'You ought to know. But as for what they are doing, do not call it living.'

A silence fell suddenly between us which I somehow expected to be unbroken. But it had not fallen for more than a few seconds when, in the utter stillness, I distinctly heard a very rapid step coming nearer and nearer along the street. The next moment a figure flung itself into the shop and stood framed in the doorway. He wore a large white hat tilted back as if in impatience; he had tight black old-fashioned pantaloons, a gaudy old-fashioned stock and waistcoat, and an old fantastic coat. He had large, wide open, luminous eyes like those of an arresting actor; he had a pale, nervous face, and a fringe of beard. He took in the shop and the old man in a look that seemed literally a flash and uttered the exclamation of a man utterly staggered.

'Good lord!' he cried out; 'it can't be you! It isn't you! I came to ask where your grave was.'

'I'm not dead yet, Mr Dickens,' said the old gentleman, with a feeble smile; 'but I'm dying,' he hastened to add reassuringly.

'But, dash it all, you were dying in my time,' said Mr Charles Dickens with animation; 'and you don't look a day older.'

'I've felt like this for a long time,' said Father Christmas.

Mr Dickens turned his back and put his head out of the door into the darkness.

'Dick,' he roared at the top of his voice; 'he's still alive.'

Another shadow darkened the doorway, and a much larger and more full-blooded gentleman in an enormous periwig came in, fanning his flushed face with a military hat of the cut of Queen Anne. He carried his head well back like a soldier, and his hot face had even a look of arrogance, which was suddenly contradicted by his eyes, which were literally as humble as a dog's. His sword made a great clatter, as if the shop were too small for it.

'Indeed,' said Sir Richard Steele, ''tis a most prodigious matter, for the man was dying when I wrote about Sir Roger de Coverley and his Christmas Day.'

My senses were growing dimmer and the room darker. It seemed to be filled with newcomers.

'It hath ever been understood,' said a burly man, who carried his head humorously and obstinately a little on one side (I think he was Ben Jonson). 'It hath ever been understood, consule Jacobo, under our King James and her late Majesty, that such good and hearty customs were fallen sick, and like to pass from the world. This grey beard most surely was no lustier when I knew him than now.'

And I also thought I heard a green-clad man, like Robin Hood, say in some mixed Norman French, 'But I saw the man dying.'

'I have felt like this a long time,' said Father Christmas, in his feeble way again.

Mr Charles Dickens suddenly leant across to him.

'Since when?' he asked. 'Since you were born?'

'Yes,' said the old man, and sank shaking into a chair. 'I have been always dying.'

Mr Dickens took off his hat with a flourish like a man calling a mob to rise.

'I understand it now,' he cried, 'you will never die.'

Christmas is a Debauch

George Orwell

Tribune, 20 December 1946
An advertisement in my Sunday paper sets forth in the form of a picture the four things that are needed for a successful Christmas. At the top of the picture is a roast turkey; below that, a Christmas pudding: below that, a dish of mince pies; and below that, a tin of Andrews Liver Salt.

It is a simple recipe for happiness. First the meal, then the antidote, then another meal. The ancient Romans were the great masters of this technique. However, having just looked up the word *vomitorium* in the Latin dictionary, I find that, after all it does *not* mean a place where you went to be sick after dinner. So perhaps this was not a normal feature of every Roman home, as is commonly believed.

Implied in the above-mentioned advertisement is the notion that a good meal means a meal at which you overeat yourself. In principle I agree. I only add in passing that when we gorge ourselves this Christmas, if we do get the chance to gorge ourselves, it is worth giving a thought to the thousand million human beings, or thereabouts, who will be doing no such thing. For in the long run our Christmas dinners would be safer if we could make sure that everyone else had a Christmas dinner as well. But I will come back to that presently.

The only reasonable motive for not overeating at Christmas would be that somebody else needs the food more than you do. A deliberately austere Christmas would be an absurdity. The whole point of Christmas is that it is a debauch – as it was probably long before the birth of Christ was arbitrarily fixed at that date. Children know this very well. From their point of view Christmas is not a day of temperate enjoyment, but of fierce pleasures which they are quite willing to pay for with a certain amount of pain. The awakening at about 4 a.m. to inspect your stocking; the quarrels over toys all through the morning, and the exciting whiffs of mincemeat and sage-and-onions escaping from the kitchen door: the battle with enormous platefuls of turkey, and the pulling of the wishbone; the darkening of the windows and the entry of the flaming plum pudding: the hurry to make sure that everyone has a piece on his plate while the brandy is still alight; the momentary panic when it is rumoured that Baby has swallowed the threepenny bit; the stupor all through the afternoon; the Christmas cake with almond icing an inch thick: the peevishness next morning and the castor oil on December 27th – it is an up-and-down business, by no means all pleasant, but well worth while for the sake of its more dramatic moments.

Glutton's Paradise

from *An Autobiography*, Agatha Christie

Christmas we used to spend in Cheshire . . . at Abney Hall, with the old Wattses and their four children and Jack. It was a wonderful house to have Christmas in if you were a child. Not only was it enormous Victorian Gothic, with quantities of rooms, passages, unexpected steps, back staircases, front staircases, alcoves, niches – everything in the world that a child could want – but it also had three different pianos that you could play, as well as an organ. All it lacked was the light of day; it was remarkably dark, except for the big drawing room with its green satin walls and its big windows . . .

Abney was a glutton's paradise. Mrs Watts had what was called her storeroom off the hall. It was not like Grannie's storeroom, a kind of securely locked treasure house from which things were taken out. There was free access to it, and all round the walls were shelves covered with every kind of dainty. One side was entirely chocolates, boxes of them, all different, chocolate creams in labelled boxes . . . There were biscuits, gingerbread, preserved fruits, jams and so on.

Christmas was the supreme Festival, something never to be forgotten. Christmas stockings in bed. Breakfast, when everyone had a separate chair heaped with presents. Then a rush to church and back to continue present opening. At two o'clock Christmas Dinner, the blinds drawn down and glittering ornaments and lights. First, oyster soup (not relished by me), turbot, then boiled turkey, roast turkey, and a large roast sirloin of beef. This was followed by plum pudding, mince pies, and a trifle full of sixpences, pigs, rings, bachelors' buttons and all the rest of it. After that, again, innumerable kinds of dessert. In a story I once wrote, *The Affair of the Christmas Pudding*, I have described just such a feast. It is one of those things that I am sure will never be seen again in this generation; indeed I doubt nowadays if anyone's digestion would stand it. However, *our* digestions stood it quite well then.

I usually had to vie in eating prowess with Humphrey Watts, the Watts son next to James in age. I suppose he must have been twenty-one or twenty-two to my twelve or thirteen. He was a very handsome young man, as well as being a good actor and a wonderful entertainer and teller of stories. Good as I always was at falling in love with people, I don't think I fell in love with him, though it is amazing to me that I should *not* have done so. I suppose I was still at the stage where my love affairs had to be romantically impossible – concerned with public characters, such as the Bishop of London and King Alfonso of Spain, and of course with various actors. I know I fell deeply in love with Henry Ainley when I saw him in *The Bondman*, and I must have been just getting ripe for the KOWS (Keen on Wallers), who were all to a girl in love with Lewis Waller in *Monsieur Beaucaire*.

Humphrey and I ate solidly through the Christmas Dinner. He scored over me in oyster soup, but otherwise we were neck and neck. We both first had roast turkey, then boiled turkey, and finally four or five slashing slices of sirloin of beef. It is possible that our elders confined themselves to only one kind of turkey for this course, but as far as I remember old Mr Watts certainly had beef as well as turkey. We then ate plum pudding and mince pies and trifle – I rather sparingly of trifle, because I didn't like the taste of wine. After that there were the crackers, the grapes, the oranges, the Elvas plums, the Carlsbad plums, and the preserved fruits. Finally, during the afternoon, various handfuls of chocolates were fetched from the storeroom to suit our taste. Do I remember being sick the next day? Having bilious attacks? No, never. The only bilious attacks I ever remember were those that seized me after eating unripe apples in September. I ate unripe apples practically every day, but occasionally I must have overdone it . . .

On Boxing Day we were always taken to the pantomime in Manchester – and very good pantomimes they were. We would come back in the train singing all the songs, the Watts rendering the comedian's songs in broad Lancashire. I remember us all bawling out: '*I was born on a Friday, I was born on a Friday, I was born on a Friday when* (crescendo!) *my mother wasn't at 'ome!*' Also: '*Watching the trains coom in, watching the trains go out, when we'd watched all the trains coom in, we watched the trains go* OUT.' The supreme favourite was sung by Humphrey as a melancholy solo: '*The window, The window, I've pushed it through the window. I have no pain, dear Mother now, I've pushed it through the window.*'

The Manchester pantomime was not the earliest I was taken to. The first I ever saw was at Drury Lane, where I was taken by Grannie. Dan Leno was Mother Goose. I can still remember that pantomime. I dreamt of Dan Leno for weeks afterwards – I thought he was the most wonderful person I had ever seen. And there was an exciting incident that night. The two little Royal princes were up in the Royal Box. Prince Eddy, as one spoke of him colloquially, dropped his programme and opera glasses over the edge of the box. They fell in the stalls quite near where we were sitting, and, oh delight, not the Equerry but Prince Eddy *himself* came down to retrieve them, apologising very politely, saying that he did hope they hadn't hurt anyone.

I went to sleep that night indulging in the fantasy that one day I would marry Prince Eddy. Possibly I could save his life from drowning first . . . A grateful Queen would give her Royal Consent. Or perhaps there would be an accident – he would be bleeding to death, I would give a blood transfusion. I would be created a Countess – like the Countess Torby – and there would be a Morganatic Marriage. Even for six years old, however, such a fantasy was a little too fantastic to last.

BOXING DAY TO EPIPHANY

An Intense Frost

from *Kilvert's Diary*

Curate to the Vicar of Clyro in Radnorshire (now Powys), Reverend Francis Kilvert's diaries reflect rural life in the 1870s. They were published over fifty years after his death.

1870

Sunday, Christmas Day

As I lay awake praying in the early morning I thought I heard a sound of distant bells. It was an intense frost. I sat down in my bath upon a sheet of thick ice which broke in the middle into large pieces whilst sharp points and jagged edges stuck all round the sides of the tub like *chevaux de frise*, not particularly comforting to the naked thighs and loins, for the keen ice cut like broken glass. The ice water stung and scorched like fire. I had to collect the floating pieces of ice and pile them on a chair before I could use the sponge and then I had to thaw the sponge in my hands for it was a mass of ice. The morning was most brilliant. Walked to the Sunday School with Gibbing – and the road sparkled with millions of rainbows, the seven colours gleaming in every glittering point of hoar frost. The Church was very cold in spite of two roaring stove fires. Mr V. preached and went to Bettws.

Monday, 26 December

Much warmer and almost a thaw. Left Clyro at 11 a.m.

At Chippenham my father and John were on the platform. After dinner we opened a hamper of game sent by the Venables, and found in it a pheasant, a hare, a brace of rabbits, a brace of woodcocks, and a turkey. Just like them, and their constant kindness.

Tuesday, 27 December

After dinner drove into Chippenham with Perch and bought a pair of skates at Benk's for 17/6. Across the fields to the Draycot water and the young Awdry ladies chaffed me about my new skates. I had not been on skates since I was here last, 5 years ago, and was very awkward for the first ten minutes, but the knack soon came again. There was a distinguished company on the ice, Lady Dangan, Lord and Lady Royston and Lord George Paget all skating. Also Lord and Lady Sydney and a Mr Calcroft, whom they all of course called the Hangman. I had the honour of being knocked down by Lord Royston, who was coming round suddenly on the outside edge. A large fire of logs burning within an enclosure of wattled hurdles. Harriet Awdry skated beautifully and jumped over a half sunken punt. Arthur Law skating jumped over a chair on its legs.

Wednesday, 28 December

An inch of snow fell last night and as we walked to Draycot to skate the snow storm began again. As we passed Langley Burrell Church we heard the strains of the quadrille band on the ice at Draycot. The afternoon grew murky and when we began to skate the air was thick with falling snow. But it soon stopped and gangs of labourers were at work immediately sweeping away the new fallen snow and skate cuttings of ice. The Lancers was beautifully skated. When it grew dark the ice was lighted with Chinese lanterns, and the intense glare of blue, green, and crimson lights and magnesium riband made the whole place as light as day. Then people skated with torches.

Thursday, 29 December

Skating at Draycot again with Perch. Fewer people on the ice today. No quadrille band, torches or fireworks, but it was very pleasant, cosy and sociable. Yesterday when the Lancers was being skated Lord Royston was directing the figures. Harriet Awdry corrected him in one figure and he was quite wrong. But he immediately left the quadrille and sat down sulking on the bank, saying to one of his friends, 'Those abominable Miss Awdrys have contradicted me about the Lancers.' This was overheard and repeated to Harriet by a mutual friend, and the next time she saw him she said meaningly, 'Lord Royston, sometimes remarks are overheard and repeated,' or something to that effect. However, soon after he wanted to make it up and asked her to skate up the ice hand in hand with him. 'Certainly not, Lord Royston,' she said. Lady Royston skates very nicely and seems very nice. A sledge chair was put on the ice and Lady Royston and Lady Dangan, Margaret, Fanny, Maria, and Harriet Awdry were drawn about in it by turns, Charles Awdry pushing behind and Edmund and Arthur and Walter pulling with ropes. It was a capital team and went at a tremendous pace up and down the ice.

1871

Monday, Christmas Day. A dark rainy morning, most un-Christmaslike. I preached the Christmas sermon in the morning, and my Father read prayers. There was no afternoon service. My father gave notice in the morning that there would be none. The Church cold and damp, and the gallery still standing. A small congregation and few communicants.

1873

7 January – At 8 o'clock Fanny, Dora and I went to a jolly party at Sir John Awdry's at Notton House. Almost everybody in the neighbourhood was there. There had been a children's party with a Christmas Tree at 5 o'clock, but when we drove up the harp and the fiddles were going. 'Bang went the drum, the ball opened immediately, and I knew not which dancer most to admire,' but I think it was – Francie Rooke. Dear little Francie Rooke. The dining room was turned into the ball room, beautifully lighted overhead, and the smooth polished oaken floor went magnificently, just like glass, but not a bit too slippery, though Eliza Styles came down with a crash full on her back in Sir Roger de Coverly, and there was a roar of laughter which, combined with Eliza's fall, shook the room.

I danced a Lancers with Harriet Awdry of Draycot Rectory, a quadrille with Sissy Awdry of Seagry Vicarage, a Lancers with Louise Awdry of Draycot Rectory, a Lancers with Mary Rooke of the Ivy, and Sir Roger with dear little Francie Rooke of the Ivy. How bright and pretty she looked, so merry, happy and full of fun. It was a grand Sir Roger. I never danced such a one. The room was quite full, two sets and such long lines, but the crush was all the more fun. 'Here,' said Francie Rooke to me quietly, with a wild, merry sparkle in her eye, and her face brilliant with excitement, 'let us go into the other set.' There was more fun going on there, Eliza Styles had just fallen prostrate. There were screams of laughter and the dance was quite wild. There was a struggle for the corners and everyone wanted to be at the top. In a few minutes all order was lost, and everyone was dancing wildly and promiscuously with whoever came to hand. The dance grew wilder and wilder. 'The pipers loud and louder blew, the dancers quick and quicker flew.' Madder and madder screamed the flying fiddle bows. Sir Roger became a wild romp till the fiddles suddenly stopped dead and there was a scream of laughter. Oh, it was such fun and Francie Rooke was brilliant. When shall I have another such partner as Francie Rooke?

An excellent supper and we got home about one o'clock, on a fine moonlit night.

1874

Thursday, Christmas Eve 1874. Writing Christmas letters all the morning. In the afternoon I went to the Church with Dora and Teddy to put up Christmas decorations. Dora had been very busy for some days past making the straw letters for the Christmas text. Fair Rosamund and good Elizabeth Knight came to the Church to help us and worked heartily and well. They had made some pretty ivy knots and bunches for the pulpit panels and the ivy blossoms cleverly whitened with flour looked just like white flowers.

The churchwarden Jacob Knight was sitting by his sister in front of the roaring fire. We were talking of the death of Major Torrens on the ice at Corsham pond yesterday. Speaking of people slipping and falling on ice the good churchwarden sagely remarked, 'Some do fall on their faces and some do fall on their rumps. And they as do hold their selves uncommon stiff do most in generally fall on their rumps.'

I took old John Bryant a Christmas packet of tea and sugar and raisins from my Mother. The old man had covered himself almost entirely over in his bed to keep himself warm, like a marmot in its nest. He said, 'If I live till New Year's Day I shall have seen ninety-six New Years.' He said also, 'I do often see things flying about me, thousands and thousands of them about half the size of a large pea, and they are red, white, blue, and yellow and all colours. I asked Mr Morgan what they were and he said they were the spirits of just men made perfect.'

Sir Gawain and the Green Knight

Anon

This King lay royally at Camelot at Christmas tide
With many fine lords, the best of men,
All the rich brethren of the Round Table,
With right rich revel and careless mirth.
There full many heroes tourneyed betimes,
Jousted full gaily; then returned these gentle knights
To the court to make carols.
For there the feast was held full fifteen days alike
With all the meat and the mirth that men could devise.
Such a merry tumult, glorious to hear;
Joyful din by day, dancing at night.
All was high joy in halls and chambers
With lords and ladies as pleased them best.
With all the weal in the world they dwelt there together,
The most famous knights save only Christ,
The loveliest ladies that ever had life,
And he, the comeliest of kings, who holds the court.
For all this fair company were in their prime in the hall,
The happiest troop under heaven
With the proudest of kings.

Truly it would be hard to name anywhere
So brave a band.

Thank You Letter

Sylvia Townsend Warner

Dearest Alyse,

Usually one begins a thank-letter by some graceless comparison, by saying, I have never been given such a very scarlet muffler, or, This is the largest horse I have ever been sent for Christmas. But your matchbox is a nonpareil, for never in my life have I been given a matchbox. Stamps, yes, drawing-pins, yes, balls of string, yes, yes, menacingly too often; but never a matchbox. Now that it has happened I ask myself why it has never happened before. They are such charming things, neat as wrens, and what a deal of ingenuity and human artfulness has gone into their construction; for if they were like the ordinary box with a lid they would not be one half so convenient. This one though is especially neat, charming, and ingenious, and the tray slides in and out as though Chippendale had made it.

But what I like best of all about my matchbox is that it is an empty one. I have often thought how much I should enjoy being given an empty house in Norway, what pleasure it would be to walk into those bare wood-smelling chambers, walls, floor, ceiling, all wood, which is after all the natural shelter of man, or at any rate the most congenial. And when I opened your matchbox which is now my matchbox and saw that beautiful clean sweet-smelling empty rectangular expanse it was exactly as though my house in Norway had come true; with the added advantage of being just the right size to carry in my hand. I shut my imagination up in it instantly, and it is still sitting there, listening to the wind in the firwood outside. Sitting there in a couple of days time I shall hear the Lutheran bell calling me to go and sing Lutheran hymns while the pastor's wife gazes abstractedly at her husband in a bower of evergreen while she wonders if she remembered to put pepper in the goose-stuffing; but I shan't go, I shall be far too happy sitting in my house that Alyse gave me for Christmas.

Oh, I must tell you I have finished my book – begun in 1941 and a hundred times imperilled but finished at last. So I can give an undivided mind to enjoying my matchbox.

(Signed)

P.S. There is still so much to say ... carried away by my delight in form and texture I forgot to praise the picture on the back. I have never seen such an agreeable likeness of a hedgehog, and the volcano in the background is magnificent.

Season's Greetings

G. Fletcher

I remember, I remember
Nothing further after that,
But I wakened in the morning
On an alien lobby mat;
And I felt not unpersuaded
(Thought my reasons were not clear)
That I'd spent a Merry Christmas
And a prosperous New Year.

The Fool Plough

from *Observations on the Popular Antiquities*
of Great Britain, John Brand

In the North of England there is a custom used at or about this time, which, as will be seen, was anciently observed also in the beginning of Lent. The *Fool Plough* goes about, a pageant that consists of a number of *sword dancers dragging a Plough*, with music, and one, sometimes two, in a very strange attire; the Bessy, in the grotesque habit of an old woman, and the Fool, almost covered with skins, a hairy cap on, and the tail of some animal hanging down his back. The office of any one of these characters, in which he is very assiduous, is to go about rattling a box amongst the spectators of the dance, in which he receives their little donations.

The Adventure of the Blue Carbuncle

Arthur Conan Doyle

I had called upon my friend Sherlock Holmes upon the second morning after Christmas, with the intention of wishing him the compliments of the season. He was lounging upon the sofa in a purple dressing-gown, a pipe-rack within his reach upon the right, and a pile of crumpled morning papers, evidently newly studied, near at hand. Beside the couch was a wooden chair, and on the angle of the back hung a very seedy and disreputable hard felt hat, much the worse for wear, and cracked in several places. A lens and a forceps lying upon the seat of the chair suggested that the hat had been suspended in this manner for the purpose of examination.

'You are engaged,' said I; 'perhaps I interrupt you.'

'Not at all. I am glad to have a friend with whom I can discuss my results. The matter is a perfectly trivial one' (he jerked his thumb in the direction of the old hat), 'but there are points in connection with it which are not entirely devoid of interest, and even of instruction.'

I seated myself in his armchair, and warmed my hands before his crackling fire, for a sharp frost had set in, and the windows were thick with the ice crystals. 'I suppose,' I remarked, 'that, homely as it looks, this thing has some deadly story linked on to it – that it is the clue which will guide you in the solution of some mystery, and the punishment of some crime.'

'No, no. No crime,' said Sherlock Holmes, laughing. 'Only one of those whimsical little incidents which will happen when you have four million human beings all jostling each other within the space of a few square miles. Amid the action and reaction of so dense a swarm of humanity, every possible combination of events may be expected to take place, and many a little problem will be presented which may be striking and bizarre without being criminal. We have already had experience of such.'

'So much so,' I remarked, 'that, of the last six cases which I have added to my notes, three have been entirely free of any legal crime.'

'Precisely. You allude to my attempt to recover the Irene Adler papers, to the singular case of Miss Mary Sutherland, and to the adventure of the man with the twisted lip. Well, I have no doubt that this small matter will fall into the same innocent category. You know Peterson, the commissionaire?'

'Yes.'

'It is to him that this trophy belongs.'

'It is his hat.'

'No, no; he found it. Its owner is unknown. I beg that you will look upon it, not as a battered billycock, but as an intellectual problem. And, first as to how it came here. It arrived upon Christmas morning, in company with a good fat goose, which is, I have no doubt, roasting at this moment in front of Peterson's fire. The facts are these. About four o'clock on Christmas morning, Peterson, who, as you know, is a very honest fellow, was returning from some small jollification, and was making his way homewards down Tottenham Court Road. In front of him he saw, in the gaslight, a tallish man, walking with a slight stagger, and carrying a white goose slung over his shoulder. As he reached the corner of Goodge Street a row broke out between this stranger and a little knot of roughs. One of the latter knocked off the man's hat, on which he raised his stick to defend himself, and, swinging it over his head, smashed the shop window behind him. Peterson had rushed forward to protect the stranger from his assailants, but the man, shocked at having broken the window and seeing an official-looking person in uniform rushing towards him, dropped his goose, took to his heels, and vanished amid the labyrinth of small streets which lie at the back of Tottenham Court Road. The roughs had also fled at the appearance of Peterson, so that he was left in possession of the field of battle, and also of the spoils of victory in the shape of this battered hat and a most unimpeachable Christmas goose.'

'Which surely he restored to their owner?'

'My dear fellow, there lies the problem. It is true that "For Mrs Henry Baker" was printed upon a small card which was tied to the bird's left leg, and it is also true that the initials "H.B." are legible upon the lining of this hat; but, as there are some thousands of Bakers, and some hundreds of Henry Bakers in this city of ours, it is not easy to restore lost property to any one of them.'

'What, then, did Peterson do?'

'He brought round both hat and goose to me on Christmas morning, knowing that even the smallest problems are of interest to me. The goose we retained until this morning, when there were signs that, in spite of the slight frost, it would be well that it should be eaten without unnecessary delay. Its finder has carried it off therefore to fulfil the ultimate destiny of a goose, while I continue to retain the hat of the unknown gentleman who lost his Christmas dinner.'

'Did he not advertise?'

'No.'

'Then, what clue could you have as to his identity?'

'Only as much as we can deduce.'

'From his hat?'

'Precisely.'

'But you are joking. What can you gather from this old battered felt?'

'Here is my lens. You know my methods. What can you gather yourself as to the individuality of the man who has worn this article?'

I took the tattered object in my hands, and turned it over rather ruefully. It was a very ordinary black hat of the usual round shape, hard and much the worse for wear. The lining had been of red silk, but was a good deal discoloured. There was no maker's name; but, as Holmes had remarked, the initials 'H.B.' were scrawled upon one side. It was pierced in the brim for a hat-securer, but the elastic was missing. For the rest, it was cracked, exceedingly dusty, and spotted in several places, although there seemed to have been some attempt to hide the discoloured patches by smearing them with ink.

'I can see nothing,' said I, handing it back to my friend.

'On the contrary Watson, you can see everything. You fail, however, to reason from what you see. You are too timid in drawing your inferences.'

'Then, pray tell me what it is that you can infer from this hat?'

He picked it up, and gazed at it in the peculiar introspective fashion which was characteristic of him. 'It is perhaps less suggestive than it might have been,' he remarked, 'and yet there are a few inferences which are very distinct, and a few others which represent at least a strong balance of probability. That the man was highly intellectual is of course obvious upon the face of it, and also that he was fairly well-to-do within the last three years, although he has now fallen upon evil days. He had foresight, but has less now than formerly, pointing to a moral retrogression, which, when taken with the decline of his fortunes, seems to indicate some evil influence, probably drink, at work upon him. This may account also for the obvious fact that his wife has ceased to love him.'

'My dear Holmes!'

'He has, however, retained some degree of self-respect,' he continued, disregarding my remonstrance. 'He is a man who leads a sedentary life, goes out little, is out of training entirely, is middle-aged, has grizzled hair which he has had cut within the last few days, and which he anoints with lime-cream. These are the more patent facts which are to be deduced from his hat. Also, by the way, that it is extremely improbable that he has gas laid on in his house.'

'You are certainly joking, Holmes.'

'Not in the least. Is it possible that even now when I give you these results you are unable to see how they are attained?'

'I have no doubt that I am very stupid; but I must confess that I am unable to follow you. For example, how did you deduce that this man was intellectual?'

For answer Holmes clapped the hat upon his head. It came right over the forehead and settled upon the bridge of his nose. 'It is a question of cubic capacity,' said he: 'a man with so large a brain must have something in it.'

'The decline of his fortunes, then?'

'This hat is three years old. These flat brims curled at the edge came in then. It is a hat of the very best quality. Look at the band of ribbed silk, and the excellent lining. If this man could afford to buy so expensive a hat three years ago, and has had no hat since, then he has assuredly gone down in the world.'

'Well, that is clear enough certainly. But how about the foresight, and the moral retrogression?'

Sherlock Holmes laughed. 'Here is the foresight,' said he, putting his finger upon the little disc and loop of the hat-securer. 'They are never sold upon hats. If this man ordered one, it is a sign of a certain amount of foresight, since he went out of his way to take this precaution against the wind. But since we see that he has broken the elastic, and has not troubled to replace it, it is obvious that he has less foresight now than formerly, which is a distinct proof of a weakening nature. On the other hand, he has endeavoured to conceal some of these stains upon the felt by daubing them with ink, which is a sign that he has not entirely lost his self-respect.'

'Your reasoning is certainly plausible.'

'The further points, that he is middle-aged, that his hair is grizzled, that it has been recently cut, and that he uses lime-cream, are all to be gathered from a close examination of the lower part of the lining. The lens discloses a large number of hair-ends, clean cut by the scissors of the barber. They all appear to be adhesive, and there is a distinct odour of lime-cream. This dust, you will observe, is not the gritty, grey dust of the street, but the fluffy brown dust of the house, showing that it has been hung up indoors most of the time; while the marks of moisture upon the inside are proof positive that the wearer perspired very freely, and could, therefore, hardly be in the best of training.'

'But his wife – you said that she had ceased to love him.'

'This hat has not been brushed for weeks. When I see you, my dear Watson, with a week's accumulation of dust upon your hat, and when your wife allows you to go out in such a state, I shall fear that you also have been unfortunate enough to lose your wife's affection.'

'But he might be a bachelor.'

'Nay, he was bringing home the goose as a peace offering to his wife. Remember the card upon the bird's leg.'

'You have an answer to everything. But how on earth do you deduce that the gas is not laid on in the house?'

'One tallow stain, or even two, might come by chance; but, when I see no less than five, I think that there can be little doubt that the individual must be brought into frequent contact with burning tallow – walks upstairs at night probably with his hat in one hand and a guttering candle in the other. Anyhow, he never got tallow stains from a gas jet. Are you satisfied?'

'Well, it is very ingenious,' said I, laughing; 'but since, as you said just now, there has been no crime committed, and no harm done save the loss of a goose, all this seems to be rather a waste of energy.'

Sherlock Holmes had opened his mouth to reply, when the door flew open, and Peterson the commissionaire rushed into the compartment with flushed cheeks and the face of a man who is dazed with astonishment.

'The goose, Mr Holmes! The goose, sir!' he gasped.

'Eh! What of it, then? Has it returned to life, and flapped off through the kitchen window?' Holmes twisted himself round upon the sofa to get a fairer view of the man's excited face.

'See here, sir! See what my wife found in its crop!' He held out his hand, and displayed upon the centre of the palm a brilliantly scintillating blue stone, rather smaller than a bean in size, but of such purity and radiance that it twinkled like an electric point in the dark hollow of his hand.

Sherlock Holmes sat up with a whistle. 'By Jove, Peterson,' said he, 'this is treasure-trove indeed! I suppose you know what you have got?'

'A diamond, sir! A precious stone! It cuts into glass as though it were putty.'

'It's more than a precious stone. It's *the* precious stone.'

'Not the Countess of Morcar's blue carbuncle?' I ejaculated.

'Precisely so. I ought to know its size and shape, seeing that I have read the advertisement about it in *The Times* every day lately. It is absolutely unique, and its value can only be conjectured, but the reward offered of a thousand pounds is certainly not within a twentieth part of the market price.'

'A thousand pounds! Great Lord of mercy!' The commissionaire plumped down into a chair, and stared from one to the other of us.

'That is the reward, and I have reason to know that there are sentimental considerations in the background which would induce the Countess to part with half of her fortune if she could but recover the gem.'

'It was lost, if I remember aright, at the Hotel Cosmopolitan,' I remarked.

'Precisely so, on the twenty-second of December, just five days ago. John Horner, a plumber, was accused of having abstracted it from the lady's jewel-case. The evidence against him was so strong that the case has been referred to the Assizes. I have some account of the matter here, I believe.' He rummaged amid his newspapers, glancing over the dates, until at last he smoothed one out, doubled it over, and read the following paragraph:

'Hotel Cosmopolitan Jewel Robbery. John Horner, 26, plumber, was brought up upon the charge of having upon the 22nd inst., abstracted from the jewel-case of the Countess of Morcar the valuable gem known as the blue carbuncle. James Ryder, upper-attendant at the hotel, gave his evidence to the effect that he had shown Horner up to the dressing-room of the Countess of Morcar upon the day of the robbery, in order that he might solder the second bar of the grate, which was loose. He had remained with Horner some little time but had finally been called away. On returning he found that Horner had disappeared, that the bureau had been forced open, and that the small morocco casket in which, as it afterwards transpired, the Countess was accustomed to keep her jewel, was lying empty upon the dressing-table. Ryder instantly gave the alarm, and Horner was arrested the same evening; but the stone could not be found either upon his person or in his rooms. Catherine Cusak, maid to the Countess, deposed to having heard Ryder's cry of dismay on discovering the robbery, and to having rushed into the room, where she found matters were as described by the last witness. Inspector Bradstreet, B Division, gave evidence as to the arrest of Horner, who struggled frantically, and protested his innocence in the strongest terms. Evidence of a previous conviction for robbery having been given against the prisoner, the magistrate refused to deal summarily with the offence, but referred it to the Assizes. Horner, who had shown signs of intense emotion during the proceedings, fainted away at the conclusion, and was carried out of court.'

'Hum! So much for the police-court,' said Holmes thoughtfully, tossing aside his paper. The question for us now to solve is the sequence of events leading from a rifled jewel-case at one end to the crop of a goose in Tottenham Court Road at the other. You see, Watson, our little deductions have suddenly assumed a much more important and less innocent aspect. Here is the stone; the stone came from the goose, and the goose came from Mr Henry Baker, the gentleman with the bad hat and all the other characteristics with which I have bored you. So now we must set ourselves very seriously to finding this gentleman, and ascertaining what part he has played in this little mystery. To do this, we must try the simplest means first, and these lie undoubtedly in an advertisement in all the evening papers. If this fail, I shall have recourse to other methods.'

'What will you say?'

'Give me a pencil, and that slip of paper. Now, then: "Found at the corner of Goodge Street, a goose and a black felt hat. Mr Henry Baker can have the same by applying at 6.30 this evening at 221B Baker Street." That is clear and concise.'

'Very. But will he see it?'

'Well, he is sure to keep an eye on the papers, since, to a poor man, the loss was a heavy one. He was clearly so scared by his mischance in breaking the window, and by the approach of Peterson, that he thought of nothing but flight; but since then he must have bitterly regretted the impulse which caused him to drop his bird. Then, again, the introduction of his name will cause him to see it, for every one who knows him will direct his attention to it. Here you are, Peterson, run down to the advertising agency, and have this put in the evening papers.'

'In which, sir?'

'Oh, in the *Globe, Star, Pall Mall, St James's Gazette, Evening News, Standard, Echo,* and any others that occur to you.'

'Very well, sir. And this stone?'

'Ah, yes, I shall keep the stone. Thank you. And, I say, Peterson, just buy a goose on your way back, and leave it here with me, for we must have one to give to this gentleman in place of the one which your family is now devouring.'

When the commissionaire had gone, Holmes took up the stone and held it against the light. 'It's a bonny thing,' said he. 'Just see how it glints and sparkles. Of course it is a nucleus and focus of crime. Every good stone is. They are the devil's pet baits. In the larger and older jewels every facet may stand for a bloody deed. This stone is not yet twenty years old. It was found in the banks of the Amoy River in Southern China, and is remarkable in having every characteristic of the carbuncle, save that it is blue in shade, instead of ruby red. In spite of its youth, it has already a sinister history. There have been two murders, a vitriol-throwing, a suicide, and several robberies brought about for the sake of this forty-grain weight of crystallized charcoal. Who would think that so pretty a toy would be a purveyor to the gallows and the prison? I'll lock it up in my strong-box now, and drop a line to the Countess to say that we have it.'

'Do you think this man Horner is innocent?'

'I cannot tell.'

'Well, then, do you imagine that this other one, Henry Baker, had anything to do with the matter?'

'It is, I think, much more likely that Henry Baker is an absolutely innocent man, who had no idea that the bird which he was carrying was of considerably more value than if it were made of solid gold. That, however, I shall determine by a very simple test, if we have an answer to our advertisement.'

'And you can do nothing until then?'

'Nothing.'

'In that case I shall continue my professional round. But I shall come back in the evening at the hour you have mentioned, for I should like to see the solution of so tangled a business.'

'Very glad to see you. I dine at seven. There is a woodcock, I believe. By the way, in view of recent occurrences, perhaps I ought to ask Mrs Hudson to examine its crop.'

I had been delayed at a case, and it was a little after half-past when I found myself in Baker Street once more. As I approached the house I saw a tall man in a Scotch bonnet, with a coat which was buttoned up to his chin, waiting outside in the bright semicircle which was thrown from the fanlight. Just as I arrived, the door was opened, and we were shown up together to Holmes's room.

'Mr Henry Baker, I believe,' said he, rising from his arm-chair, and greeting his visitor with the easy air of geniality which he could so readily assume. 'Pray take this chair by the fire, Mr Baker. It is a cold night, and I observe that your circulation is more adapted for summer than for winter. Ah, Watson, you have just come at the right time. Is that your hat, Mr Baker?'

'Yes, sir, that is undoubtedly my hat.'

He was a large man, with rounded shoulders, a massive head, and a broad, intelligent face, sloping down to a pointed beard of grizzled brown. A touch of red in nose and cheeks, with a slight tremor of his extended hand, recalled Holmes's surmise as to his habits. His rusty black frock-coat was buttoned right up in front, with the collar turned up, and his lank wrists protruded from his sleeves without a sign of cuff or shirt. He spoke in a low staccato fashion, choosing his words with care, and gave the impression generally of a man of learning and letters who had had ill-usage at the hands of fortune.

'We have retained these things for some days,' said Holmes, 'because we expected to see an advertisement from you giving your address. I am at a loss to know now why you did not advertise.'

Our visitor gave a rather shamefaced laugh. 'Shillings have not been so plentiful with me as they once were,' he remarked. 'I had no doubt that the gang of roughs who assaulted me had carried off both my hat and the bird. I did not care to spend more money in a hopeless attempt at recovering them.'

'Very naturally. By the way, about the bird – we were compelled to eat it.'

'To eat it!' Our visitor half rose from his chair in his excitement.

'Yes; it would have been no use to anyone had we not done so. But I presume that this other goose upon the sideboard, which is about the same weight and perfectly fresh, will answer your purpose equally well?'

'Oh, certainly, certainly!' answered Mr Baker, with a sigh of relief.

'Of course, we still have the feathers, legs, crop, and so on of your own bird, if you so wish . . .'

The man burst into a hearty laugh. 'They might be useful to me as relics of my adventure,' said he, 'but beyond that I can hardly see what use the *disjecta membra* of my late acquaintance are going to be to me. No, sir, I think that, with your permission, I will confine my attentions to the excellent bird which I perceive upon the sideboard.'

Sherlock Holmes glanced across at me with a slight shrug of his shoulders.

'There is your hat, then, and there your bird,' said he. 'By the way, would it bore you to tell me where you got the other one from? I am somewhat of a fowl fancier, and I have seldom seen a better-grown goose.'

'Certainly, sir,' said Baker, who had risen and tucked his newly gained property under his arm. 'There are a few of us who frequent the Alpha Inn near the Museum – we are to be found in the Museum itself during the day, you understand. This year our good host, Windigate by name, instituted a goose-club, by which, on consideration of some few pence every week, we were to receive a bird at Christmas. My pence were duly paid, and the rest is familiar to you. I am much indebted to you, sir, for a Scotch bonnet is fitted neither to my years nor my gravity.' With a comical pomposity of manner he bowed solemnly to both of us, and strode off upon his way.

'So much for Mr Henry Baker,' said Holmes, when he had closed the door behind him. 'It is quite certain that he knows nothing whatever about the matter. Are you hungry, Watson?'

'Not particularly.'

'Then I suggest that we turn our dinner into a supper, and follow up this clue while it is still hot.'

'By all means.'

It was a bitter night, so we drew on our ulsters and wrapped cravats about our throats. Outside, the stars were shining coldly in a cloudless sky, and the breath of the passers-by blew out into smoke like so many pistol shots. Our footfalls rang out crisply and loudly as we swung through the doctors' quarter, Wimpole Street, Harley Street, and so through Wigmore Street into Oxford Street. In a quarter of an hour we were in Bloomsbury at the Alpha Inn, which is a small public house at the corner of one of the streets which run down into Holborn. Holmes pushed open the door of the private bar, and ordered two glasses of beer from the ruddy-faced, white-aproned landlord.

'Your beer should be excellent if it is as good as your geese,' he said.

'My geese!' The man seemed surprised.

'Yes. I was speaking only half an hour ago to Mr Henry Baker, who was a member of your goose-club.'

'Ah! yes, I see. But you see, sir. them's not *our* geese.'

'Indeed! Whose, then?'

'Well, I get the two dozen from a salesman in Covent Garden.'

'Indeed! I know some of them. Which was it?'

'Breckinridge is his name.'

'Ah! I don't know him. Well, here's your good health, landlord, and prosperity to your house. Good night.'

'Now for Mr Breckinridge,' he continued, buttoning up his coat, as we came out into the frosty air. 'Remember, Watson, that though we have so homely a thing as a goose at one end of this chain, we have at the other a man who will certainly get seven years' penal servitude, unless we can establish his innocence. It is possible that our inquiry may but confirm his guilt; but, in any case, we have a line of investigation which has been missed by the police, and which a singular chance has placed in our hands. Let us follow it out to the bitter end. Faces to the south, then, and quick march!'

We passed across Holborn, down Endell Street, and so through a zigzag of slums to Covent Garden Market. One of the largest stalls bore the name of Breckinridge upon it, and the proprietor, a horsy-looking man, with a sharp face and trim side-whiskers, was helping a boy to put up the shutters.

'Good evening. It's a cold night,' said Holmes.

The salesman nodded, and shot a questioning glance at my companion.

'Sold out of geese, I see,' continued Holmes, pointing at the bare slabs of marble.

'Let you have five hundred tomorrow morning.'

'That's no good.'

'Well, there are some on the stall with the gas fire.'

'Ah, but I was recommended to you.'

'Who by?'

'The landlord of the "Alpha".'

'Ah, yes; I sent him a couple of dozen.'

'Fine birds they were, too. Now where did you get them from?'

To my surprise the question provoked a burst of anger from the salesman.

'Now then, mister,' said he, with his head cocked and his arms akimbo, 'what are you driving at? Let's have it straight, now.'

'It is straight enough. I should like to know who sold you the geese which you supplied to the "Alpha".'

'Well, then, I shan't tell you. So now!'

'Oh, it is a matter of no importance; but I don't know why you should be so warm over such a trifle.'

'Warm! You'd be as warm, maybe, if you were as pestered as I am. When I pay good money for a good article there should be an end to the business; but it's "Where are the geese?" and "Who did you sell the geese to?" and "What will you take for the geese?" One would think they were the only geese in the world, to hear the fuss that is made over them.'

'Well, I have no connection with any other people who have been making inquiries,' said Holmes carelessly. 'If you won't tell us the bet is off, that is all. But I'm always ready to back my opinion on a matter of fowls, and I have a fiver on it that the bird I ate is country bred.'

'Well, then, you've lost your fiver, for it's town bred,' snapped the salesman.

'It's nothing of the kind.'

'I say it is.'

'I don't believe you.'

'D'you think you know more about fowls than I, who have handled them ever since I was a nipper? I tell you, all those birds that went to the "Alpha" were town bred.'

'You'll never persuade me to believe that.'

'Will you bet, then?'

'It's merely taking your money, for I know that I am right. But I'll have a sovereign on with you, just to teach you not to be obstinate.'

The salesman chuckled grimly. 'Bring me the books, Bill,' said he.

The small boy brought round a small thin volume and a great greasy-backed one, laying them out together beneath the hanging lamp.

'Now then, Mr Cocksure,' said the salesman, 'I thought that I was out of geese, but before I finish you'll find that there is still one left in my shop. You see this little book?'

'Well?'

'That's the list of the folk from whom I buy. D'you see? Well, then, here on this page are the country folk, and the numbers after their names are where their accounts are in the big ledger.

Now, then! You see this other page in red ink? Well, that is a list of my town suppliers. Now, look at that third name. Just read it out to me.'

'Mrs Oakshott, 117 Brixton Road – 249,' read Holmes.

'Quite so. Now turn that up in the ledger.'

Holmes turned to the page indicated. 'Here you are, "Mrs Oakshott, 117 Brixton Road, egg and poultry supplier." '

'Now, then, what's the last entry?'

' "December 22. Twenty-four geese at 7s. 6d." '

'Quite so. There you are. And underneath?'

' "Sold to Mr Windigate of the 'Alpha' at 12s." '

'What have you to say now?'

Sherlock Holmes looked deeply chagrined. He drew a sovereign from his pocket and threw it down upon the slab, turning away with the air of a man whose disgust is too deep for words. A few yards off he stopped under a lamp-post, and laughed in the hearty, noiseless fashion which was peculiar to him.

'When you see a man with whiskers of that cut and the "Pink 'Un" protruding out of his pocket, you can always draw him by a bet,' said he. 'I dare say that if I had put a hundred pounds down in front of him that man would not have given me such complete information as was drawn from him by the idea that he was doing me on a wager. Well, Watson, we are, I fancy, nearing the end of our quest, and the only point which remains to be determined is whether we should go on to this Mrs Oakshott tonight, or whether we should reserve it for tomorrow. It is clear from what that surly fellow said that there are others besides ourselves who are anxious about the matter, and I should . . .'

His remarks were suddenly cut short by a loud hubbub which broke out from the stall which we had just left. Turning round we saw a little rat-faced fellow standing in the centre of the circle of yellow light which was thrown by the swinging lamp, while Breckinridge the salesman, framed in the door of his stall, was shaking his fists fiercely at the cringing figure.

'I've had enough of you and your geese,' he shouted. 'I wish you were all at the devil together. If you come pestering me any more with your silly talk I'll set the dog at you. You bring Mrs Oakshott here and I'll answer her, but what have you to do with it? Did I buy the geese off you?'

'No; but one of them was mine all the same,' whined the little man.

'Well, then, ask Mrs Oakshott for it.'

'She told me to ask you.'

'Well, you can ask the King of Proosia, for all I care. I've had enough of it. Get out of this!' He rushed fiercely forward, and the inquirer flitted away into the darkness.

'Ha, this may save us a visit to Brixton Road,' whispered Holmes. 'Come with me, and we will see what is to be made of this fellow.' Striding through the scattered knots of people who lounged round the flaring stalls, my companion speedily over-took the little man and touched him upon the shoulder. He sprang round, and I could see in the gaslight that every vestige of colour had been driven from his face.

'Who are you, then? What do you want?' he asked in a quavering voice.

'You will excuse me,' said Holmes blandly, 'but I could not help overhearing the questions which you put to the salesman just now. I think that I could be of assistance to you.'

'You? Who are you? How could you know anything of the matter?'

'My name is Sherlock Holmes. It is my business to know what other people don't know.'

'But you can know nothing of this?'

'Excuse me, I know everything of it. You are endeavouring to trace some geese which were sold by Mrs Oakshott, of Brixton Road, to a salesman named Breckinridge, by him in turn to Mr Windigate, of the "Alpha," and by him to his club, of which Mr Henry Baker is a member.'

'Oh, sir, you are the very man whom I have longed to meet,' cried the little fellow, with outstretched hands and quivering fingers. 'I can hardly explain to you how interested I am in this matter.'

Sherlock Holmes hailed a four-wheeler which was passing. 'In that case we had better discuss it in a cosy room rather than in this windswept marketplace,' said he. 'But pray tell me, before we go further, who it is that I have the pleasure of assisting.'

The man hesitated for an instant. 'My name is John Robinson,' he answered, with a sidelong glance.

'No, no; the real name,' said Holmes sweetly. 'It is always awkward doing business with an *alias*.'

A flush sprang to the white cheeks of the stranger. 'Well, then,' said he, 'my real name is James Ryder.'

'Precisely so. Head attendant at the Hotel Cosmopolitan. Pray step into the cab, and I shall soon be able to tell you everything which you would wish to know.'

The little man stood glancing from one to the other of us with half-frightened, half-hopeful eyes, as one who is not sure whether he is on the verge of a windfall or of a catastrophe. Then he stepped into the cab, and in half an hour we were back in the sitting-room at Baker Street. Nothing had been said during our drive, but the high, thin breathings of our new companion, and the claspings and unclaspings of his hands, spoke of the nervous tension within him.

'Here we are!' said Holmes cheerily, as we filed into the room. 'The fire looks very seasonable in this weather. You look cold, Mr Ryder. Pray take the basket chair. I will just put on my slippers before we settle this little matter of yours. Now, then! You want to know what became of those geese?'

'Yes, sir.'

'Or rather, I fancy, of that goose. It was one bird, I imagine, in which you were interested – white, with a black bar across the tail.'

Ryder quivered with emotion. 'Oh, sir,' he cried, 'can you tell me where it went to?'

'It came here.'

'Here?'

'Yes, and a most remarkable bird it proved. I don't wonder that you should take an interest in it. It laid an egg after it was dead – the bonniest, brightest little blue egg that ever was seen. I have it here in my museum.'

Our visitor staggered to his feet, and clutched the mantelpiece with his right hand. Holmes unlocked his strong-box, and held up the blue carbuncle, which shone out like a star, with a cold, brilliant, many-pointed radiance. Ryder stood glaring with a drawn face, uncertain whether to claim or to disown it.

'The game's up, Ryder,' said Holmes quietly. 'Hold up, man, or you'll be into the fire. Give him an arm back into his chair, Watson. He's not got blood enough to go in for felony with impunity. Give him a dash of brandy. So! Now he looks a little more human. What a shrimp it is, to be sure!'

For a moment he had staggered and nearly fallen, but the brandy brought a tinge of colour into his cheeks, and he sat staring with frightened eyes at his accuser.

'I have almost every link in my hands, and all the proofs which I could possibly need, so there is little which you need tell me. Still, that little may as well be cleared up to make the case complete. You had heard, Ryder, of this blue stone of the Countess of Morcar's?'

'It was Catherine Cusack who told me of it,' said he, in a crackling voice.

'I see. Her ladyship's waiting-maid. Well, the temptation of sudden wealth so easily acquired was too much for you, as it has been for better men before you; but you were not very scrupulous in the means you used. It seems to me, Ryder, that there is the making of a very pretty villain in you. You knew that this man Horner, the plumber, had been concerned in some such matter before, and that suspicion would rest the more readily upon him. What did you do, then? You made some small job in my lady's room – you and your confederate Cusack – and you managed that he should be the man sent for. Then, when he had left, you rifled the jewel-case, raised the alarm, and had this unfortunate man arrested. You then . . .'

Ryder threw himself down suddenly upon the rug, and clutched at my companion's knees. 'For God's sake, have mercy!' he shrieked. 'Think of my father! Of my mother! It would break their hearts. I never went wrong before! I never will again. I swear it. I'll swear it on a Bible. Oh, don't bring it into court! For Christ's sake, don't!'

'Get back into your chair!' said Holmes sternly. 'It is very well to cringe and crawl now, but you thought little enough of this poor Horner in the dock for a crime of which he knew nothing.'

'I will fly, Mr Holmes. I will leave the country, sir. Then the charge against him will break down.'

'Hum! We will talk about that. And now let us hear a true account of the next act. How came the stone into the goose, and how came the goose into the open market? Tell us the truth, for there lies your only hope of safety.'

Ryder passed his tongue over his parched lips. 'I will tell you it just as it happened, sir,' said he. 'When Horner had been arrested, it seemed to me that it would be best for me to get away with the stone at once, for I did not know at what moment the police might not take it into their heads to search me and my room. There was no place about the hotel where it would be safe. I went out, as if on some commission, and I made for my sister's house. She had married a man named

Oakshott, and lived in Brixton Road, where she fattened fowls for the market. All the way there every man I met seemed to me to be a policeman or a detective, and for all that it was a cold night, the sweat was pouring down my face before I came to the Brixton Road. My sister asked me what was the matter, and why I was so pale; but I told her that I had been upset by the jewel robbery at the hotel. Then I went into the backyard, and smoked a pipe, and wondered what it would be best to do.

'I had a friend once called Maudsley, who went to the bad, and has just been serving his time in Pentonville. One day he had met me, and fell into talk about the ways of thieves and how they could get rid of what they stole. I knew that he would be true to me, for I knew one or two things about him, so I made up my mind to go right on to Kilburn, where he lived, and take him into my confidence. He would show me how to turn the stone into money. But how to get to him in safety? I thought of the agonies I had gone through in coming from the hotel. I might at any moment be seized and searched, and there would be the stone in my waistcoat pocket. I was leaning against the wall at the time, and looking at the geese which were waddling about round my feet, and suddenly an idea came into my head which showed me how I could beat the best detective that ever lived.

'My sister had told me some weeks before that I might have the pick of her geese for a Christmas present, and I knew that she was always as good as her word. I would take my goose now, and in it I would carry my stone to Kilburn. There was a little shed in the yard, and behind this I drove one of the birds, a fine big one, white, with a barred tail. I caught it and, prising its bill open, I thrust the stone down its throat as far as my finger could reach. The bird gave a gulp, and I felt the stone pass along its gullet and down into its crop. But the creature flapped and struggled, and out came my sister to know what was the matter. As I turned to speak to her the brute broke loose, and fluttered off among the others.

' "Whatever were you doing with that bird, Jem?" says she.

' "Well," said I, "you said you'd give me one for Christmas, and I was feeling which was the fattest."

' "Oh," says she, "we've set yours aside for you. Jem's bird, we call it. It's the big, white one over yonder. There's twenty-six of them, which makes one for you, and one for us, and two dozen for the market."

' "Thank you, Maggie," says I; "but if it is all the same to you I'd rather have that one I was handling just now."

' "The other is a good three pound heavier," she said, "and we fattened it expressly for you."

' "Never mind. I'll have the other, and I'll take it now," said I.

' "Oh, just as you like," said she, a little huffed. "Which is it you want, then?"

' "That white one, with the barred tail, right in the middle of the flock."

' "Oh, very well. Kill it and take it with you."

'Well, I did what she said, Mr Holmes, and I carried the bird all the way to Kilburn. I told my pal what I had done, for he was a man that it was easy to tell a thing like that to. He laughed until he choked, and we got a knife and opened the goose. My heart turned to water, for there was no sign of the stone, and I knew that some terrible mistake had occurred. I left the bird, rushed back to my sister's, and hurried into the backyard. There was not a bird to be seen there.

' "Where are they all, Maggie?" I cried.

' "Gone to the dealer's."

' "Which dealer's?"

' "Breckinridge, of Covent Garden."

' "But was there another with a barred tail?" I asked, "the same as the one I chose?"

' "Yes, Jem, there were two barred tailed ones, and I could never tell them apart."

'Well, then, of course, I saw it all, and I ran off as hard as my feet would carry me to this man Breckinridge; but he had sold the lot at once, and not one word would he tell me as to where they had gone. You heard him yourselves tonight. Well, he has always answered me like that. My sister thinks that I am going mad. Sometimes I think that I am myself. And now – and now I am myself a branded thief, without ever having touched the wealth for which I sold my character. God help me! God help me!' He burst into convulsive sobbing, with his face buried in his hands.

There was a long silence, broken only by his heavy breathing, and by the measured tapping of Sherlock Holmes's fingertips upon the edge of the table. Then my friend rose, and threw open the door.

'Get out!' said he.

'What, sir! Oh, Heaven bless you!'

'No more words. Get out!'

And no more words were needed. There was a rush, a clatter upon the stairs, the bang of a door, and the crisp rattle of running footfalls from the street.

'After all, Watson,' said Holmes, reaching up his hand for his clay pipe, 'I am not retained by the police to supply their deficiencies. If Horner were in danger it would be another thing, but this fellow will not appear against him, and the case must collapse. I suppose that I am commuting a felony, but it is just possible that I am saving a soul. This fellow will not go wrong again. He is too terribly frightened. Send him to gaol now, and you make him a gaolbird for life. Besides, it is the season of forgiveness. Chance has put in our way a most singular and whimsical problem, and its solution is its own reward. If you will have the goodness to touch the bell, Doctor, we will begin another investigation, in which also a bird will be the chief feature.'

Like a Christmas Comedy

from *Love's Labour's Lost*, William Shakespeare

PRINCESS   Pardon me, sir, this jewel did she wear;
  And Lord Berowne, I thank him, is my dear.
  What, will you have me, or your pearl again?
BEROWNE   Neither of either; I remit both twain.
  I see the trick on't: here was a consent,
  Knowing aforehand of our merriment,
  To dash it like a Christmas comedy.

These Strained Rejoicings

from *The Letters*, D. H. Lawrence

22 December 1918, Middleton-by-Wirksworth, Derby . . . The weather is very dark and nasty, and Christmas is an institution that really should be abolished. I don't want to hear of it, it wearies me – I suppose you will be in town, tripping round and refusing turkey. But one needs spring to come, when the skies will lift a bit and one can wander forth . . .

27 December 1918, Ripley, nr. Derby . . . My God, what masses of food here, turkey, large tongues, long wall of roast loin of pork,

pork pies, sausages, mince pies, dark cakes covered with almonds, cheesecakes, lemon tarts, jellies, endless masses of food, with whisky, gin, port wine, burgundy, muscatel. It seems incredible. We played charades – the old people of 67 playing away harder than the young ones – and lit the Christmas tree, and drank healths, and sang, and roared – Lord above. If only one hadn't all the while a sense that next week would be the same dreariness as before. What a good party we might have had, had we felt really free of the world . . .

29 December 1925, Spotorno, Genova . . . I haven't heard from anybody – drew an almost blank Christmas. Just as well, for I hate these strained rejoicings . . .

December 1929, Bandol . . . Well, here's Xmas in a day or two! – I rather hate it. Why make merry when one doesn't feel merry. However, my sisters have sent plum pudding and cake, so I suppose we'll invite the friends and eat it appropriately . . .

23 December 1929, Bandol . . . I think you're lucky to escape the Christmassing. Why do we do it! But I suppose the children like it. – I'm keeping ours down to a mere tea party, so not much harm done . . .

A Christmas Present

G. K. Chesterton

A person of great generosity has given me for a Christmas present an enormous resplendent walking-stick – with silver bands, a shiny handle, and all sorts of things I had never heard of. Its splendour, indeed, creates a kind of problem. The walking-stick and I do not suit each other. The only question is, which shall give way? May it not reasonably be supposed that after a few days in my company the walking-stick may take on a more dingy, battered, and comfortable look? Or must I dress up to the walking-stick? In the fairy tales (on which I rely more and more) the touch of a wand can turn the Beast into a beautiful Prince. Perhaps the touch of this stick can turn the beast now under discussion into a beautiful dandy. Already I feel vaguely that I ought to have one neat kid glove with which to hold the stick. From this it is but a step to having good cuffs and shirt-links, and so the creeping paralysis of propriety may crawl up my arms and cover my whole person. In a year or so the stick may have transformed me wholly into its own image. Whether this will ever happen I do not know. What I do know is that if I walk down the streets with the stick at present most people mistake me for a tramp who has stolen a gentleman's walking-stick.

After earnest thought, prayer, and meditation, I have come to the conclusion that it is my destiny in life to be a foil to the stick. I am only a background – a gloomy, a rugged background – against which the stick picks itself out in sparkling purity and distinctness. I suppose the strict grammatical definition of a walking-stick is a stick that can walk. I am sure this stick can walk by itself; I am merely a large, florid tassle attached to it. The people of Battersea will merely praise the stick as they see it passing along the street. Then, when their admiration of it is exhausted (if that be conceivable) they may add: 'And how artistic an idea to tie to this walking-stick an ill-dressed and unattractive human being, thus celebrating supremely in an image the victory of the inanimate over the animate.' I exist only in order to throw up the high light upon the lustrous stick. What matters it that I am abased so long as It is exalted. At any rate, this simple resolution to be a background to the stick is much less terrible than the other idea of living up to it.

I Sat Next to the Duchess

from *The Wandering Years: Diaries 1922–39*, Cecil Beaton

[December 1931] Margaret Drummond-Hay is golden-haired, with love-in-the-mist eyes and russet cheeks. She has masses of equally healthy-looking giants for brothers. They troop over to me for charades on Saturday evenings, and we often ride together on the downs. Margaret has even introduced me to the pleasures of the Hunt.

Today's invitation was from the mother (whom I had never met) of these athletic, God-like creatures. I had heard that her husband, the Duke, was a cripple, that he had been paralysed after falling from the mast of a ship. I knew well of the Duchess being a rabid humanitarian and anti-vivisectionist, and that she had turned Ferne into a sort of dogs' home. In fact, any stray that finds its way through these remote Wiltshire lanes to this ugly Victorian mansion, whether it be a human refugee, discarded pet bird, donkey, monkey, or mongrel is sure of a welcome.

Today the school-like dining room was alive with children and dogs. What with all the young sons and daughters of the house, and their pets, and with the addition of many guests of all denominations, the floor seemed to be a sea of moving limbs and paws. Children, on all fours, scrambled under tables, together with the dogs and cats who gnawed at the remains from table and filled in every cubic inch of space. I sat next to the Duchess, a tall woman of independent character rather than of the classical beauty unexpectedly apparent in her children. She was dressed in white summer clothes as is her custom throughout the year. It is her perpetual expression of mourning for one of her young children who died tragically.

We tried to talk about books, but our attempts at conversation were constantly interrupted by animals and children of various sizes and shapes.

At last we found ourselves marshalled into the drawing room, where a spindly Christmas tree stood decorated with tinsel toys and illuminated by coloured bulbs. Soon the village children from Berwick St John trooped in by invitation – fifty or sixty of them standing like a military unit. They had large heads, pale, weedy complexions, and goggle eyes. An overfat schoolmaster, crimson in the face, conducted a hymn while his minions sang with only a remote interest in the proceedings.

The Duchess stood to attention surrounded by many ugly, grey-haired women, including a few deaf mutes. The village children, puny and unattractive, made a startling contrast to the healthy ducal offspring.

Her Grace then spoke a few words, welcoming the local children and giving them a dissertation on the advantages of country over city. Each leaf, she explained, was different in the country. There were many things to watch; they must appreciate and preserve its rustic joys.

One boy was asked the main difference between town and country and ruggedly replied, 'Oi think the moine difference is that in the cities there is so much dust and doirt and muck. In the country, the air is different and there are flewers.'

'Quite right, that is excellent.' The Duchess seemed a stalking crane in her off-white flannel skirt, socks and gym shoes. Finally she excoriated those who are cruel to the animals. 'Above all you must be kind to birds.'

The children were then encouraged to give bird calls for Father Christmas. They moved joylessly into the pitchpine panelled hall and intoned at the top of their melancholy screechy voices. After delays, and hitches and whispered commands from the family, and repeated shouts in unison from the children, Father Christmas materialised in the form of the Duke who was wheeled on to the scene by Geordie, his stalwart son. The Duke was dressed in red flannel with hood and a wig of white cotton-wool. The children were told to line up in order of their ages. Those who were twelve years old must head the procession and be given a present.

A few mumbled words, then the village children were given orders to troop as a platoon into the frigid drawing room. Each child took an orange and an apple from fruit-filled Tate sugar boxes placed near the door.

Everyone waited: grey-haired women, deaf mutes, refugee cats and dogs, and children of all ages. Then the lights went out; a few of the smaller village children began to whimper. The ducal grandchildren crawled in and out of legs, human and animal, while outside the French windows their handsome parents could be seen for a flash or two, as they ran in the stormy darkness with matches and beacons. Suddenly a Catherine wheel hissed; then in the rain appeared a shower of 'golden rain'; squibs popped; jumping crackers exploded on the wet ground; Chinese crackers went off in a series of half-hearted reports.

The whimpering village children now burst into screams of alarm. Terrified of the darkness and the noise, they howled, bellowed, shrieked with each new explosion. Babies cried, dogs barked, oranges and apples rolled on the floor. From exploding rockets blinding flashes revealed a maggot-crawling mass of panicking children and dogs. The hysteria reached a terrifying crescendo when a spurting, spluttering 'sparkler' came flying indoors.

Princess Margaret's Christmas Present List

Princess Elizabeth

This Christmas list was compiled by the ten-year-old Princess Elizabeth to help her six-year-old sister Princess Margaret write her thank-you letters.

Present	Given by
See-saw	Mummie
Dolls with dresses	"
Umbrella	Papa
Teniquoit	"
Brooch	Mummie
Calendar	Grannie
Silver Coffee Pot	*Lilibet*
Clock	*to*
Puzzle	*Margaret*
Pen and Pencil	Equerry
China Field Mice	M.E.
Bag and Cricket set	Boforts
Electric Stove	David B.L.
China Lamb	Linda

1914: A Point of View

from *The Times*, A. Clutton-Brock

WE have all read what happened between the opposing armies, and how it came unexpected, undesigned, and yet willed with all the unconscious force of their natures. Not once or twice but again and again we hear of this sudden change upon the night of Christmas Eve, how there was singing upon one side answered by the other, and how the men rose and advanced to meet each other as if they had been released from a spell. Everyone who tells of it speaks also of his own wonder as if he had seen a miracle; and some say that the darkness became strange and beautiful with lights as well as music, as if the armies had been gathered together there not for war but for the Christmas feast . . . The Prussian thinks that if only he is brutal enough he will cease to be ridiculous. When will Germany cease to be a monster of his creation? When will she regain the humanity of those soldiers of hers who made friends with ours on Christmas Day? We cannot tell; but we can at least refrain from delaying that time by telling her, and believing ourselves, that she is no longer human to us, that her crimes are inexpiable, and that Europe is committed to an everlasting blood-feud with her. That is not what our soldiers say; they were ready to forgive at the Christmas truce; they sang their hymns of peace, and at the sound of them war seemed unreal, and soldiers were no longer soldiers, but men.

Letter home from Ceylon

Flying Officer Harold Gardner

This letter was written home to Flying Officer Harold Gardner's sister Mabel while he was serving with Section 16, RAF Ceylon in 1944.

Thank you for your Christmas Airgraph & for your letter (no. 30) of 5th November enclosing copy of Trinity Magazine. Regarding the latter I'm sorry you went to the expense of sending it by air mail; it is hardly quicker than sea mail – Edna & I found that out long ago & seldom make use of the service. You see this one took seven weeks! Well, my last Christmas overseas, and my best, is over. Let me tell you about it. It actually started for me several days before Christmas for I always think that the preparation is more pleasurable than the event itself. We – the Rover Crew – thought we'd hold our own party on Christmas night. Our fellows are all decent chaps who object to the horseplay & drunkenness that are always the outstanding feature of Christmas at any camp, so we decided to get away from it. I was in charge of 'effects' – but, unfortunately, the town is out of bounds owing to an outbreak of smallpox, so that I could not purchase anything, & we had to improvise. It saved money, & we had the fun of making things. We made paper chains by cutting up coloured covers of magazines & by painting scrap paper; we decorated the Radjan walls with fronds of palm leaves; we made memento cards for autographs; &, above all, we hewed down a cactus bush which we used as a Christmas tree, & it was just perfect with bonbons (which we were fortunate to obtain), & small gifts of cigarettes, razor blades, & c. & c. which we purchased from our NAAFI. In fact I really think the cactus is better than a spruce fir – it carries the weight better – but I guarantee it's the first time in history that a cactus has been used for this purpose! We had the whole photographed (indoors) – I hope the result will be good.

On Christmas evening, then, after a reasonably good dinner in the Mess, 26 of us adjourned to the Hut, & we stayed there until 2 a.m.! We played games & sang songs & carols – &, of course, smoked & drank 'pop', & ate tinned fruit, & biscuits, & peanuts! It was <u>very</u> successful indeed – & will, I'm sure, strengthen the Crew for the future, apart from being a Happy Christmas. I helped to serve the airmen with their Christmas dinner in traditional Service style. On Sunday evening we had a Carol Service – the first service in our Camp Church. The Church is yet another Radjan but adapted for the purpose, & the furnishings are the work of the men. It holds about *100*, & was full! There were other services, & sports events, & cinema shows & concerts on the camp – but other duties or other preferences didn't allow me, of course, to be at them all. Anyhow it was a very good Christmas, & I trust it was for you also.

Boxing Day Hangover

from *The Bettesworth Book*, George Sturt

December 27. The weather has remained so wonderfully mild, or 'open', as we say, that outdoor work has received no serious check, and the labouring people were better prepared to face Christmas than it is their wont to be. Bettesworth, amongst others, has had plenty to do, as I have been able to keep him employed.

But looking for him this morning, after the two days' holiday, I discovered him at work in his own part of the garden.

'Oh; going to dig that up this morning?' I asked.

'Ah, it looked so ontidy. An' I ben't jest up to the mark; so I thought I'd have a smack at this.'

Observing him more narrowly, I saw that he looked pale and gently sick. 'Feel a bit Christmassy?' I said.

He looked ashamed, and answered with a feeble smile. 'That is it, sir, to tell ye the truth . . . Some o' my mates with their wives come round to my place last night. They wanted me to goo round to they; but I says, "No; I en't goin' out. You best come an' see me." So they all come, an' we made a reg'lar evenin' of it.'

'You've been having a merry Christmas, then?'

'Oh, there's no mistake about that. We did enjoy ourselves. One or two brought a bottle o' home-made wine; an' then there was a jug o' beer, an' so on . . . But I ben't fit for much 's mornin'. I come an' made a start as soon's 'twas light; but my 'ead was that queer there 't seemed all mops and brooms. So I says to my ol' gal, "I shall do a bit o' my own today."'

'Perhaps you were up late?'

'Ah, we was. Past the turn o' the night. Turn o' the night? What be I talkin' of? 'Twas two o'clock afore we broke up.' (Remember that during the winter Bettesworth is generally in bed by half-past eight or nine o'clock.) 'An' we did git merry, too. Got to singin' at last.'

'Oh! You did go it. We were pretty quiet, up here.'

'Well, there didn't seem to be nothin' gwine on nowhere. I come out once while they was singin'. An' all up the valley was as quiety . . . There didn't seem to be nobody about, an' nothin' gwine on nowheres, 'xcept 'twas at my place. But I heerd ol' Biggs – my neighbour, ye know – sayin', "What! Bettesworth's got a party of 'em, then! That's the fust time since we bin here." An' when I went indoors agen, I says to 'em, "You be disturbin' the neighbours." But we did enjoy ourselves, an' no mistake.'

I tried to imagine the jolly party: eight of them in a little stuffy room, with a paraffin lamp and the reek of tobacco smoke to aid the fire in keeping them warm. Want of ventilation had probably more than the beer and wine to do with the old man's headache. Besides, he had had too little sleep.

'I don't wonder,' I said, 'that you feel queer, if you didn't get to bed before two o'clock.'

' 'Twas purty well three afore I got to bed . . . And then I got up . . . Well, the clock struck six, and my ol' gal she says, "There's six o'clock. Ben't ye goin' to git up?" "No," I says, "I shall have another half-hour." I wa'n't ready to turn out. An' there I laid, ontil the clock warned for seven. Then I did git out an' lit the fire. But I ses to the old gal, "My head do ache," I says. "So do mine," she says'.

The old man seemed needlessly cast down and ashamed. I tried to encourage him, and suggested that 'it'll wear off as the day goes on'.

'Oh, yes, sir! It'll wear off. Now I be about – there, I seems better a'ready. 'Twas jest at first startin' I seemed so queer. But once I can git on workin' and git into a good sweat I shall do.'

And his surmise was correct. Before night came round again, all his discomfort had vanished: and the pleasant recollections of his cheerful evening remained unsullied.

On *A Christmas Carol*

W. M. Thackeray

Who can listen to objections regarding such a book as this? It seems to me a national benefit, and to every man or woman who reads it a personal kindness. The last two people I heard speak of it were women; neither knew the other, or the author, and both said, by way of criticism, 'God bless him!' A Scotch philosopher, who nationally does not keep Christmas day, on reading the book, sent out for a turkey, and asked two friends to dine – this is a fact! Many men were known to sit down, after perusing it, and write off letters to their friends, not about business, but out of their fulness of heart, and to wish old acquaintances a happy Christmas. Had the book appeared a fortnight earlier, all the prize cattle would have been gobbled up in pure love and friendship, Epping denuded of sausages, and not a turkey left in Norfolk. His royal highness's fat stock would have fetched unheard-of prices, and Alderman Bannister would have been tired of slaying . . .

As for Tiny Tim, there is a certain passage in the book regarding that young gentleman, about which a man should hardly venture to speak in print or in public, any more than he would of any other affections of his private heart. There is not a reader in England but that little creature will be a bond of union between the author and him; and he will say of Charles Dickens, as the woman said just now, 'God bless him!' What a feeling is this for a writer to be able to inspire, and what a reward to reap!

In Memoriam

Alfred Tennyson

Ring out, wild bells, to the wild sky,
The flying cloud, the frosty light:
The year is dying in the night;
Ring out, wild bells, and let him die.

Ring out the old, ring in the new,
Ring, happy bells, across the snow:
The year is going, let him go;
Ring out the false, ring in the true.

Ring out the grief that saps the mind,
For those that here we see no more;
Ring out the feud of rich and poor,
Ring in redress to all mankind.

Ring out a slowly dying cause,
And ancient forms of party strife;
Ring in the nobler modes of life,
With sweeter manners, purer laws.

Ring out the want, the care, the sin,
The faithless coldness of the times;
Ring out, ring out my mournful rhymes,
But ring the fuller minstrel in.

Ring out false pride in place and blood,
The civic slander and the spite;
Ring in the love of truth and right,
Ring in the common love of good.

Ring out old shapes of foul disease;
Ring out the narrowing lust of gold;
Ring out the thousand wars of old,
Ring in the thousand years of peace.

Ring in the valiant man and free,
The larger heart, the kindlier hand;
Ring out the darkness of the land,
Ring in the Christ that is to be.

It is the day when he was born,
A bitter day that early sank
Behind a purple-frosty bank
Of vapour, leaving night forlorn.

The time admits not flowers or leaves
To deck the banquet. Fiercely flies
The blast of North and East, and ice
Makes daggers at the sharpen'd eaves,

And bristles all the brakes and thorns
To yon hard crescent, as she hangs
Above the wood which grides and clangs
Its leafless ribs and iron horns

Together, in the drifts that pass
To darken on the rolling brine
That breaks the coast. But fetch the wine,
Arrange the board and brim the glass;

Bring in great logs and let them lie,
To make a solid core of heat;
Be cheerful-minded, talk and treat
Of all things ev'n as he were by;

We keep the day. With festal cheer,
With books and music, surely we
Will drink to him, whate'er he be,
And sing the songs he loved to hear.

Melancholy Christmas

from *Journal to Stella*, Dean Swift

LONDON, Dec. 24, 1711. I went into the City today in a coach, and dined there. My cold is going. It is now bitter hard frost, and has been so these three or four days. . . . My lord privy-seal set out this day for Holland: he'll have a cold journey. I gave Patrick half a crown for his Christmas-box, on condition he would be good, and he came home drunk at midnight. I have taken a memorandum of it; because I never design to give him a groat more. 'Tis cruel cold.

25. I wish MD a merry Christmas, and many a one; but mine is melancholy: I durst not go to church today, finding myself a little out of order, and it snowing prodigiously, and freezing.

27. The frost still continues violently cold. Mrs Masham invited me to come tonight and play at cards; but our society did not part till nine. But I supped with Mrs Hill, her sister, and there was Mrs Masham and lord treasurer, and we stayed till twelve. He is endeavouring to get a majority against next Wednesday, when the House of lords is to meet, and the Whigs intend to make some violent addresses against a Peace, if not prevented. God knows what will become of us.

29. Saturday night. I have broke open my letter, and tore it into the bargain, to let you know that we are all safe; the queen has made no less than twelve lords to have a majority; and has turned out the Duke of Somerset. She is awaked at last, and so is lord treasurer: I want nothing now but to see the duchess [of Marlborough] out. We are all extremely happy. Give me joy, sirrahs. This is written in a coffee-house. Three of the new lords are of our Society.

30. The duke of Marlborough was at Court today, and nobody hardly took notice of him.

31. Our frost is broken since yesterday, and it is very slabbery; yet I walked into the city and dined, and ordered some things with the printer. . . . I hear the Duke of Marlborough is turned out of all his employments: I shall know tomorrow, when I am to carry Dr King to dine with the secretary.

January 1, 1712. Now I wish my dearest little MD many happy New-years; yes, both Dingley and Stella, aye, and Presto too, many happy new-years. I dined with the secretary, and it is true that the duke of Marlborough is turned out of all. The duke of Ormond has got his regiment of Footguards, I know not who has the rest. . . . The queen and lord treasurer mortally hate the duke of Marlborough, and to that he owes his fall, more than to his other faults; unless he has been tampering too far with his party, of which I have not heard any particulars; however it be, the world abroad will blame us. I confess my belief that he has not one good quality in the world besides that of a General, and even that I have heard denied by several great soldiers. But we have had constant success in arms while he commanded. Opinion is a mighty matter in war, and I doubt but the French think it impossible to conquer an army that he leads, and our soldiers think the same; and how far even this step may encourage the French to play tricks with us, no man knows. I do not love to see personal resentment mix with publick affairs.

A Christmas Masque

William Gershom Collingwood

THE CHORUS:
Aback of the North, where Yule is Yule,
And winter snowy and summer cool,
(Patience, friends, if we play the fool!)
Aback of the fells, where snow lies white,
And windows shine in the fire-light,
Folk are carolling into the night.

Here together to sing together and dance together we
   meet;
Hands are ready and hearts are ready and ready are nimble
   feet;

And the piper sits with his bag blown out, piping merry
    and sweet
With a drone:
Up to the rafter, down to the hearthstone, woven mel-
    odies chime;
Figuring craftily, fading daintily, buzzing like bees in
    thyme;
Pipe the ballad and dance the measure and clap at the
    clashing rhyme,
With a drone.

      Round and round we tramp, lads,
      By the light of the flickering lamp, lads,
      And all together we stamp, lads,
      To the drone.

          The THREE KINGS *enter.*
      We be three kings come out of the East,
      Into the North for a Christmas feast,
      And all afoot for lack of a beast.
      Tinker's crown upon head we bear,
      Robe of woollen our only wear,
      And a hollin* staff for a sceptre rare.

Singing, out of the realm of Araby, out of the morning
    land,
Travelling far by firth and fell and over the sunken sand,
Hither we hie to make your merry-night; here for a
    dance we stand
To the drone:
Fluttering bagpipe, lift it, carry it, forth to a frosty moon;
Following voices, praise it, raise it, up to the stars aboon;

* Holly.

Pattering footstep, mark the measure, and clatter the
    staves in tune,
To the drone.

      And under the swinging lamp,
      Round and round we tramp,
      Turn together and stamp,
      With a drone.

Shepherds of old were sitting in fold and the stars were
    out in the sky,
Shepherding folk with a shepherd's pipe, and played as
    the stars went by;
And who be we but shepherding folk? and our pipes play
    merry and high
To the drone:
Angels out of the silver stars and a wonder of golden
    light,
Glory, sang they, praise and peace to the child that is born
    to-night!
And ever we sing their Yule-tide carol and follow the
    tune aright
With our drone:

      And softly the breezes sigh;
      And stilly the waters lie;
      And sweetly the voices die,
      With the drone.

Journey of the Magi

T.S. Eliot

'A cold coming we had of it,
Just the worst time of the year
For a journey, and such a long journey:
The ways deep and the weather sharp,
The very dead of winter.'
And the camels galled, sore-footed, refractory,
Lying down in the melting snow.
There were times we regretted
The summer palaces on slopes, the terraces,
And the silken girls bringing sherbet.
Then the camel men cursing and grumbling
And running away, and wanting their liquor and women,
And the night-fires going out, and the lack of shelters,
And the cities hostile and the towns unfriendly
And the villages dirty and charging high prices:
A hard time we had of it.
At the end we preferred to travel all night,
Sleeping in snatches,
With the voices singing in our ears, saying
That this was all folly.
Then at dawn we came down to a temperate valley,
Wet, below the snow line, smelling of vegetation,
With a running stream and a water-mill beating the
    darkness,
And three trees on the low sky.
And an old white horse galloped away in the meadow.
Then we came to a tavern with vine-leaves over the
    lintel,
Six hands at an open door dicing for pieces of silver,

And feet kicking the empty wine–skins.
But there was no information, and so we continued
And arrived at evening, not a moment too soon
Finding the place; it was (you may say) satisfactory.

All this was a long time ago, I remember,
And I would do it again, but set down
This set down
This: were we led all that way for
Birth or Death? There was a Birth, certainly,
We had evidence and no doubt. I had seen birth and
    death,
But had thought they were different; this Birth was
Hard and bitter agony for us, like Death, our death.
We returned to our places, these Kingdoms,
But no longer at ease here, in the old dispensation,
With an alien people clutching their gods.
I should be glad of another death.

The Rightwise King of All England

from *Morte d'Arthur*, Thomas Malory

Then stood the realm in great jeopardy long while, for every lord that was mighty of men made him strong, and many weened to have been king. Then Merlin went to the Archbishop of Canterbury, and counselled him for to send for all the lords of the realm, and all the gentlemen of arms, that they should to London come by Christmas, upon pain of cursing; and for this cause, that Jesus, that was born on that night, that he would of his great mercy show some miracle, as he was come to be king of mankind, for to show some miracle who should be rightwise king of this realm.

So the Archbishop, by the advice of Merlin, sent for all the lords and gentlemen of arms that they should come by Christmas even unto London. And many of them made them clean of their life, that their prayer might be the more acceptable unto God. So in the greatest church of London, whether it were Paul's or not, the French book maketh no mention, all the estates were long or day in the church for to pray. And when matins and the first mass was done, there was seen in the churchyard, against the high altar, a great stone four square, like unto a marble stone; and in midst thereof was like an anvil of steel a foot on high, and therein stuck a fair sword naked by the point, and letters there were written in gold about the sword that said thus:

WHOSO PULLETH OUT THIS SWORD OF THIS STONE AND ANVIL, IS RIGHTWISE KING BORN OF ALL ENGLAND.

Then the people marvelled, and told it to the Archbishop. 'I command', said the Archbishop, 'that ye keep you within your church and pray unto God still, that no man touch the sword till the high mass be all done.'

So when all masses were done all the lords went to behold the stone and the sword. And when they saw the scripture some assayed, such as would have been king. But none might stir the sword nor move it.

'He is not here,' said the Archbishop, 'that shall achieve the sword, but doubt not God will make him known.

'But this is my counsel,' said the Archbishop, 'that we let purvey ten knights, men of good fame, and they to keep this sword.' So it was ordained, and then there was made a cry, that every man should assay that would, for to win the sword.

And upon New Year's Day the barons let make a jousts and a tournament, that all knights that would joust or tourney there might play, and all this was ordained for to keep the lords together and the commons, for the Archbishop trusted that God would make him known that should win the sword.

So upon New Year's Day, when the service was done, the barons rode unto the field, some to joust and some to tourney, and so it happened that Sir Ector, that had great livelihood about London, rode unto the jousts, and with him rode Sir Kay his son, and young Arthur that was his nourished brother; and Sir Kay was made knight at All Hallowmass afore.

So as they rode to the jousts-ward, Sir Kay lost his sword, for he had left it at his father's lodging, and so he prayed young Arthur for to ride for his sword. 'I will well', said Arthur, and rode fast after the sword, and when he came home, the lady and all were out to see the jousting. Then was Arthur wroth, and said to himself, 'I will ride to the churchyard, and take the sword with me that sticketh in the stone, for my brother Sir Kay shall not be without a sword this day.'

So when he came to the churchyard, Sir Arthur alighted and tied his horse to the stile, and so he went to the tent, and found no knights there, for they were at the jousting. And so he handled the sword by the handles, and lightly and fiercely pulled it out of the stone, and took his horse and rode his way until he came to his brother Sir Kay, and delivered him the sword.

And as soon as Sir Kay saw the sword, he wist well it was the sword of the stone, and so he rode to his father Sir Ector, and said: 'Sir, lo here is the sword of the stone, wherefore I must be king of this land.'

When Sir Ector beheld the sword, he returned again and came to the church, and there they alighted all three, and went into the church. And anon he made Sir Kay swear upon a book how he came to that sword. 'Sir,' said Sir Kay, 'by my brother Arthur, for he brought it to me.'

'How gat ye this sword?' said Sir Ector to Arthur.

'Sir, I will tell you. When I came home for my brother's sword, I found nobody at home to deliver me his sword; and so I thought my brother Sir Kay should not be swordless, and so I came hither eagerly and pulled it out of the stone without any pain.'

'Found ye any knights about this sword?' said Sir Ector.

'Nay,' said Arthur.

'Now,' said Sir Ector to Arthur, 'I understand ye must be king of this land.'

'Wherefore I,' said Arthur, 'and for what cause?'

'Sir,' said Ector, 'for God will have it so; for there should never man have drawn out this sword, but he that shall be rightwise king of this land. Now let me see whether ye can put the sword there as it was, and pull it out again.'

'That is no mastery,' said Arthur, and so he put it in the stone; wherewithal Sir Ector assayed to pull out the sword and failed.

'Now assay,' said Sir Ector unto Sir Kay. And anon he pulled at the sword with all his might; but it would not be.

'Now shall ye assay,' said Sir Ector to Arthur.

'I will well,' said Arthur, and pulled it out easily.

And therewithal Sir Ector knelt down to the earth, and Sir Kay.

'Alas,' said Arthur, 'my own dear father and brother, why kneel ye to me?'

'Nay, nay, my lord Arthur, it is not so; I was never your father nor of your blood, but I wot well ye are of an higher blood than I weened ye were.' And then Sir Ector told him all, how he was betaken him for to nourish him, and by whose commandment, and by Merlin's deliverance . . .

Therewithal they went unto the Archbishop, and told him how the sword was achieved, and by whom; and on Twelfth-day all the barons came thither, and to assay to take the sword, who that would assay. But there afore them all, there might none take it out but Arthur; wherefore there were many lords wroth, and said it was great shame unto them all and the realm, to be overgoverned with a boy of no high blood born.

Sermon on the Journey of the Magi, 1622

Rev Lancelot Andrewes

The Rt Rev Lancelot Andrewes (1555–1626) was one of the leading churchmen of his time. During the reign of James I he was successively Bishop of Chichester, Ely and Winchester, and he was one of the principal editors of the Authorised Version of the Bible. On Christmas Day 1622 he preached a sermon before the King on 'The Journey of the Magi.' It probably lasted a good hour, but here is an abridgement by my friend Nigel Rees:

In this their coming we consider, first, the distance of the place they came from. It was not hard by as the shepherds were, but a step to Bethlehem over the fields; this was riding many hundred miles, and cost them many a day's journey. Secondly we consider the way that they came, if it be pleasant, or plain and easy; for if it be, it is so much the better. But this was nothing pleasant, for it was through deserts, all the way waste and desolate.

Nor easy neither; for over the rocks and crags of both Arabias their journey lay. And it was not safe, but exceeding dangerous, as lying through the midst of the 'black tents of Kedar', a nation of thieves and cut-throats; to pass over the hills of robbers, infamous then, and infamous to this day. Last we consider the time of their coming, the season of the year. It was no summer progress.

A cold coming they had of it at this time of the year, just the worst time of the year to take a journey, and specially a long journey. The ways deep, the weather sharp, the days short, the sun farthest off, in the very dead of winter.

And these difficulties they overcame, of a wearisome, irksome, troublesome, dangerous, unseasonable journey; and despite all this they came. And came it cheerfully and quickly, as appeareth by the speed they made. They were highly conceited of His birth, believed some great matter of it, that they took all these pains, made all this haste that they might be there to worship Him with all the possible speed they could.

And we, what should we have done? We should fairly have put the journey off to the spring of the year, till the days longer, and the ways fairer, and the weather warmer, till better travelling to Christ. Our Epiphany would sure have fallen in Easter week at the soonest.

We Three Kings

John Henry Hopkins

We three kings of Orient are;
Bearing gifts we traverse afar,
Field and fountain, moor and mountain,
Following yonder star.

O star of wonder, star of night,
Star with royal beauty bright,
Westward leading, still proceeding,
Guide us to thy perfect light.
Born a King on Bethlehem's plain
Gold I bring to crown Him again,
King forever, ceasing never,
Over us all to reign.

O star of wonder, star of night,
Star with royal beauty bright,
Westward leading, still proceeding,
Guide us to thy perfect light.

Frankincense to offer have I;
Incense owns a Deity nigh;
Prayer and praising, voices raising,
Worshiping God on high.

O star of wonder, star of night,
Star with royal beauty bright,
Westward leading, still proceeding,
Guide us to thy perfect light.

Myrrh is mine, its bitter perfume
Breathes a life of gathering gloom;
Sorrowing, sighing, bleeding, dying,
Sealed in the stone cold tomb.

O star of wonder, star of night,
Star with royal beauty bright,
Westward leading, still proceeding,
Guide us to thy perfect light.

Glorious now behold Him arise;
King and God and sacrifice;
Alleluia!, Alleluia!,
Rings through the earth and skies.

O star of wonder, star of night,
Star with royal beauty bright,
Westward leading, still proceeding,
Guide us to thy perfect light.

The Twelve Days of Christmas: A Correspondence

John Julius Norwich

25th December

My dearest darling

That partridge, in that lovely little pear tree! What an enchanting, romantic, poetic present! Bless you and thank you.

Your deeply loving Emily

26th December

My dearest darling Edward

The two turtle doves arrived this morning and are cooing away in the pear tree as I write. I'm so touched and grateful.

With undying love, as always, Emily

27th December

My darling Edward

You do think of the most original presents; whoever thought of sending anybody three French hens? Do they really come all the way from France? It's a pity that we have no chicken coops, but I expect we'll find some. Thank you, anyway, they're lovely.

Your loving Emily

28th December

Dearest Edward

What a surprise — four calling birds arrived this

morning. They are very sweet, even if they do call rather loudly – they make telephoning impossible. But I expect they'll calm down when they get used to their new home. Anyway, I've very grateful – of course I am.

Love from Emily

29th December

Dearest Edward

The postman has just delivered five most beautiful gold rings, one for each finger, and all fitting perfectly. A really lovely present – lovelier in a way than birds, which do take rather a lot of looking after. The four that arrived yesterday are still making a terrible row, and I'm afraid none of us got much sleep last night. Mummy says she wants to use the rings to 'wring' their necks – she's only joking, I think; though I know what she means. But I *love* the rings. Bless you.

Love, Emily

30th December

Dear Edward

Whatever I expected to find when I opened the front door this morning, it certainly wasn't six socking great geese laying eggs all over the doorstep. Frankly, I rather hoped you had stopped sending me birds – we have no room for them and they have already ruined the croquet lawn. I know you meant well, but – let's call a halt, shall we?

Love, Emily

31st December

Edward

I thought I said no more birds; but this morning I woke up to find no less than seven swans all trying to get into our tiny goldfish pond. I'd rather not think what happened to the goldfish. The whole house seems to be full of birds – to say nothing of what they leave behind them. Please, please STOP.

Your Emily

1st January

Frankly, I think I prefer the birds. What am I to do with eight milkmaids – AND their cows? Is this some kind of a joke? If so, I'm afraid I don't find it very amusing.

Emily

2nd January

Look here Edward, this has gone far enough. You say you're sending me nine ladies dancing; all I can say is that judging from the way they dance, they're certainly not ladies. The village just isn't accustomed to seeing a regiment of shameless hussies with nothing on but their lipstick cavorting round the green – and it's Mummy and I who get blamed. If you value our friendship – which I do less and less – kindly stop this ridiculous behaviour at once.

Emily

3rd January

As I write this letter, ten disgusting old men are prancing about all over what used to be the garden – before the geese and the swans and the cows got at it; and several of them, I notice, are taking inexcusable liberties with the milkmaids. Meanwhile the neighbours are trying to have us evicted. I shall never speak to you again.

Emily

4th January

This is the last straw. You know I detest bagpipes. The

place has now become something between a menagerie and a madhouse and a man from the Council has just declared it unfit for habitation. At least Mummy has been spared this last outrage; they took her away yesterday afternoon in an ambulance. I hope you're satisfied.

5th January

Sir

Our client, Miss Emily Wilbraham, instructs me to inform you that with the arrival on her premises at half-past seven this morning of the entire percussion section of the Liverpool Philharmonic Orchestra and several of their friends she has no course left open to her but to seek an injunction to prevent your importuning her further. I am making arrangements for the return of much assorted livestock.

I am, Sir, Yours faithfully,

G. CREEP

Solicitor-at-Law

Credits

Index